DARWIN
AND THE NAKED LADY

DARWIN

AND THE NAKED LADY

*Discursive Essays
on Biology
and Art*

by
ALEX COMFORT

LONDON
ROUTLEDGE & KEGAN PAUL

First published 1961
by Routledge & Kegan Paul Ltd
Broadway House, 68-74 Carter Lane
London, E.C.4

Printed in Great Britain
by The Garden City Press Limited
Letchworth, Hertfordshire

© Alex Comfort 1961

For Ruth

Contents

Acknowledgements

THE chapter on 'Darwin and Freud' is based on a Lecture given at University College, London, on January 19, 1960, the original text of which has appeared in *The Lancet* (1960 ii 107–111). The chapter 'The Rape of Andromeda' appeared in *Literature and Psychology* X (i) 1960, parts of the chapter 'The Naked Lady' in *The London Magazine*, and parts of the final chapter in *The Listener*.

I

On Hard and Soft Centres

Rêve et réalité—la rose et le rosier.

PAUL ELUARD

I WILL begin with two observations which look unconnected. One of the advertisers in *Nature* recently published a photograph of a solid model representing a mathematical equation, with the words 'What is a beautiful shape? Why is one shape considered attractive and another ugly? This question is one which mathematicians may soon be able to answer.' During the war I called on a fashionable novelist (you must guess his identity without my help) and found him stripped to the waist and surrounded by books on psychoanalysis which he appeared to be transcribing into his manuscript. These are two possible figures of the relationship between science and aesthetics: the second, I imagine, partly explains the unwillingness which many people feel to consider the first.

Our response to art, and our liking for producing it, as well as our response to beauty in general, are forms of behaviour. Science, in one of its commonest senses, is a technique of asking questions, and there are a great many questions about our aesthetic behaviour which nobody interested either in art or in biology can easily fail to ask. Both aesthetic appreciation, and its effects on us, are biologically rather remarkable. An audience at a concert sits for several hours listening to a sequence of sounds and rhythms which have no direct symbolic content; they may experience very intense emotions as a result—the capacity to do this is in part learned, because peoples unused to this kind of music react to it less immediately; and in part inherited, because both tone-deafness and musicality seem to have a genetic component: at the same time the tendency to like music is as nearly 'inherent' as any second-order human response, both in social and in individual development.

We might well start asking questions here, and, since some of them, including the question in the advertisement, might be answerable by experiments, there can be a biology of art, as there is a biology of digestion or of motoring. Sully and Fechter, who introduced psychology into experimental aesthetics, were looking for 'universal laws of pleasurable impression'—work of this kind still goes on, though I imagine that psychologists who undertake it have stopped looking for universal laws, like the rest of us, and are looking for regularities of behaviour instead.

With the vast exception of psychoanalysis and the ideas which spring from it, science has contributed relatively little to aesthetics by asking direct questions about it. At the same time it has altered art by altering techniques, societies and attitudes. The effects of art on science, science on art, and one or both on any convenient third object (usually society) are gravy-train subjects which belong to the closed metabolic cycle of printed and spoken matter on which whole University departments live, and I do not want to poach upon them. I shall use 'art' to mean visual and verbal construction, and 'artist' in the same sense. The context will show whether other activities can suitably be included. I imagine the main direct effect of scientific activities on art, bulk social change apart, has been in providing new experiences—far more so than new media or materials. It has, for example, greatly widened the range of ordinary people's visual experience, real and simulated: there is now less consumer-pressure on the artist to simulate reality, and at the same time there seems to be a growing preference, in literature at least, for a clear separation of the categories of experience—for actuality over fiction at one extreme, and for undisguised erotic fantasy at the other: the old and tried fantasy-reality mixture is perhaps showing signs of breaking up. If the literary symbol of nineteenth-century progress was the novel, I suspect that for the next half-century it may be twofold—the documentary and the comic-book.

If so, I am going to suggest to you that this division, which you may welcome or not, is the consumer reaction which parallels a highly important effect of science on artists. Changes of attitude in art due to scientific ideas are hard to detach from cultural history generally, though one can point to examples: apparent influences of one on the other are often illusory—what was changing was the culture as a whole. When a Darwin or a Freud produces a large change in the human self-estimate, the fact that he is able to do so shows that it was already changing, and reflecting the change simultaneously in art. The change which is occurring now is more general and probably more fundamental. Each of the three great shocks which science has administered to human self-estimates—the non-geocentric universe, evolution, and the unconscious mind—produced a stepwise change in attitudes, but their cumulative effect, and that of science as a habit of mind, is greater than any one new piece of thinking. Science has established its universal relevance, and it is this which we are beginning to feel.

Rationalism and scientific empiricism are not new, and they have affected art and artists intermittently for many years. The new factor, I think, is that in the near future, because of the direct entry of scientific products into daily life, nobody is going to be able to avoid using, sometimes at least, the methods of thought that go with them. These methods were originally developed to provide predictive answers to practical questions, justified because they succeeded in doing so, and tolerated on the assumption, tacit or spoken, that they could be kept out of matters traditionally reserved to partial, spiritual, commonsense or irrational judgment. So, by an effort of will, they can—but however strongly it is fenced, the scientific method is an addiction. Once it is acquired as a discipline in one context, we have to make an active effort of un-reason to maintain the integrity of the fencing, and prevent ourselves from beginning to apply it generally. Freud administered the last great shock to our complacency, by demonstrating the enormous resources in our minds which maintain that fencing; he has sometimes received the unthinking applause of those who wished to see the quarantine maintained—since our reason betrays us, we had better not trust it. In reality, the fence was down—if the It had been supreme, as Groddeck thought, Freud could never have unearthed it experimentally. Instead, he showed that science could and did attack the nature of the defects in its own chief instrument, by attacking the nature of human unreason—that it is stronger in sum than our individual resistances—that it cannot, in fact, be fenced. The often conspicuous unreason of scientists in matters outside their research does not negative this. A scientific training cannot give us insight or control more than a limited number of our prejudices, but yet it reduces our capacity for equivocation, even if only a little.

In suggesting what this might mean for art, I want first to draw a distinction between two ways of thinking. It represents a division which runs straight through human thought, scientific as well as artistic and philosophic, and I can best take a scientific example to illustrate it. There are two approaches to generalisation, which I will call, without prejudicial intention, hard- and soft-centred. The hard-centred approach to an observed sequence of events, a 'regularity of behaviour', is to assume, justifiably or not, that it can be 'explained'—that we can find out upon what the regularity depends. The soft-centred approach is to state the regularity, call it a law, a truth, or a spiritual reality, and treat these names as if they were explanations. Reverence is the soft-centred equivalent of curiosity.

There were two reactions to the observation that if animals are forced to live in changed conditions, they will themselves, over a few generations, change to meet them as neatly as a Grand Master changes his game when challenged. One was to carry out experiments to find out how they did so—with the conclusion that in most cases individuals which can meet the new conditions survive preferentially and leave their attributes to their progeny. The other is to put the change down to the universal will of living matter to evolve, a mind-like quality which directs organic behaviour. Darwin was hard-centred, Bergson and Driesch are soft. There are two responses to the finding—if it be true—that all men in infancy display something very like sexual jealousy against their fathers; or that some symbols have a near-universal and apparently unlearned associative meaning. One is to attribute such regularities, provisionally at least, to some feature of our instinctive development, or a property of the cerebral filing-system, and try to relate them to the behaviour of primates. The other is to analogise the body of common experience as a soul

4

which inhabits Man as personality 'inhabits' men. In the records of many thousands of business firms, the random errors which are made are inexplicably similar, the same unrelated subjects are occasionally filed together; there is an intangible system in all the responses of these unconnected concerns to stimuli from outside. It is as if they were in telepathic communication with each other—as if the ledgers had an ancestral fund of unlearned experience. They have—the IBM punch-card system is not *anima mundi*, but *anima negotii*. Its random errors have mathematical properties in two dimensions which depend, in fact, not on any Pythagorean principle, but on the spacing of punch-holes. It has inherent symbolic equivalences. The group unconscious to which it gives rise is a perfectly real entity, but a more manageable one when we guess its nature. And confronted with the regularities, but knowing nothing about punch cards, we shall, if we are hard-centred, guess at least that some kind of sorting-system is likely to be involved: if we are soft-centred, our reverence for the mystery may prevent us from guessing anything. We shall proceed in the expectation, and I think, the hope, that here, at last, is something inherent, transcendent or supernatural; we shall be looking eagerly for the pretext to stop thinking.

Freud, in such matters, was hard-centred; true, he was confused by his assumption of the Lamarckian inheritance of memories, which we should now restate in much harder-centred Darwinian terms. But he was profoundly hard-centred by inclination—one of the hardest ever, which is why he appeals more to biologists than his successors. Jung, though one can often give his ideas hard-centres by restatement, is, I think, by inclination soft-centred. The patterns he describes are real, but they often appear to represent the avoidance, not the practice, of analysis. To acquire Freud's toughness, one must be able to see human preoccupations, art among them, as interesting derivatives of primate behaviour, without once losing confidence in their value; one cannot leave any patches of straw unthreshed because God is nesting in them. The difference between mechanism and dynamism, which Jung himself mentions, is not the distinction I am drawing—there are hard- and soft-centred brands of each.

The choice of approach—and centre—is made at the very outset of thinking—in the way the hypothesis is framed and treated.

Hard-centredness assumes that what we see is due, if not to processes we know, then to intelligible processes like those we already know. Soft-centredness nourishes, often against its scientific judgment, the hope that the matter might be one before which it can relax intellectually and enjoy the emotion of awe. Hard-centred people invoke the scientific method hoping that it will succeed, soft-centred people hoping that it will fail.

Hard-centredness is itself, no doubt, a prejudgment of the issue, as we prejudge the experimental situation in trying our own keys on an unfamiliar door—on the basis that doors have keys, even if these keys do not fit this particular door. And soft-centredness is not mere illogicality. The entities in which it deals are usually quite real, though they are often sticks held by the wrong, or less profitable, end. Bergsonian vitalism is soft-centred, but the 'drive' of living matter toward greater non-randomness, its tendency to accumulate information, has indeed mind-like properties: there are contexts where the analogy could be profitable—for all we know, 'will' in human and animal behaviour might depend on some system of selection acting on a system of random variation. In that case the analogy would be exact. Most speculation in science proceeds by fitting analogies and seeing how far they will go. The evolutionary demon, the life force, the soul of the world and the Nonconformist Conscience are all real entities—as real as Venus or Kali (we ignore them at our peril); soft-centredness does not consist in seeing them, or in failing to analyse them, but in treating them as excuses, numina before which we can lay down the unwelcome burden of critical thought.

I cannot find exact philosophical names for hard- and soft-centredness. They approach the mediaeval 'ratio' and 'intelligentia'. They are attitudes, not systems, though they often generate empiricism and vitalism respectively. They have great historical importance in science—a struggle has gone on between them over successive problems of causal analysis, in evolution, genetics, embryology, psychology. The tendency to one or another is, I think, wholly a matter of personality, though soft-centredness can be hardened by discipline. Both may well have unconscious origins. The excessively hard-centred are often palpably refugees from the irrational in themselves which they are trying to control, the soft-centred from the sternness of mortality and the insecurity of being one's own master. At the same time, I see a good case beyond my own tastes for regarding soft-centred readings of events as fundamentally antiscientific. The control of the irrational is man's most important project, and the history of science is the history of numina, entelechies, inherent principles and the like submitting to restatement in terms of tangible events. After the control experiment, hard-centred attitudes are the most practically-important human discovery. The whole vast and highly intelligent structure of Chinese natural philosophy, built up by ingenious people over centuries, was sterilised, so far as application was concerned, by being soft-centred. The moral appeal of the soft-centred as 'higher', while the hard-centred is hubristic and inaesthetic, might very easily, but for cultural accidents, have had the same effects in Europe.

At the same time, if it takes hard-centred attributes to criticise ideas, it may take soft-centred attributes to see them. The soft-centred approach often depends on an unusually acute sense of significant likeness, pattern or relation, which outruns the percipient's powers of analysis. Like the failure to recall a name, or the presence of an elusive recurrence in wallpaper, this kind of awareness can be compelling and disturbing until it is brought to some sort of statement, and it can carry a strong intuitive sense of significance. Feelings of significance have a great importance in the production of art, of which I shall have more to say later—they are also important but potentially very dangerous sources of ideas in science. Once seen and stated, the discovery of the pattern, like the recollection of the forgotten name, or a completed sneeze, brings deep satisfaction—which often goes with the creation of a category or the statement of a relationship. There is something about this particular pleasure which generates strong resistance to further analysis of the way in which the pattern was constituted. It produces a disabling sense of enlightenment which is proof against argument.

The real achievement of science has lain in finding ways of determining whether our feelings of significance are relevant. Some of them—those which occur with overwhelming force as epileptic aurae, for instance, are not. One peculiarity of schizophrenic thinking is its liability to discover significant pattern which runs at right-angles to our normal categories: such pattern is certainly significant for our understanding of the mind, but the schizophrenic is apt to defend it as a revelation. An artist able to sense, but still control, perceptual thinking of this kind—Klee or Joyce, for instance, or Steinberg—can achieve some startling effects with it. The schizophrenic's disability is that he cannot switch it off.

Schizophrenic thinking is probably the softest-centred of all. Religious and political thinking is often almost equally soft-centred, but for quite a different reason—it talks in hard-centred terms, but demands an area of thought from which critical comparison with reality must be actively excluded. For centuries European thought was moulded by the need to discover some literal sense in which bread could be said to become flesh: religion and politics are, indeed, the commonest determining forces in making scientists partially soft-centred in professional contexts today.

In our culture, an artist is by long tradition expected to be soft-centred. When Havelock Ellis called Freud an artist, Freud wrote—'This is the most refined and amiable form of resistance, calling me a great artist in order to injure the validity of our scientific claims!'[1] That which is art is traditionally not science, and probably not true.

Now there is certainly a similarity between some features of soft-centred science (intuitive perception of pattern, the sense of significance that goes with such perceptions, the tendency to keep them as pets and the reluctance to dissect them when caught) and the experience of many artists. But to equate the two, and call soft-centredness artistic and hard-centredness scientific, is not quite accurate. Art and science are different, or complementary, activities which are intended to do quite different things. They are represented as competing only by soft-centred people who would like to see the prestige of hard-centredness deflated, and by hard-centred people who have misunderstood what art is attempting.

Science is committed to the reality-principle. It has to be, for when it is not it fails to work, and that failure will be evident to the simplest person. If we reject Mendel as bourgeois, we find we have no beef. If we make non-Einsteinian radio valves we will have no radio. It is as simple as that, though occasionally the failure takes time to show. The set of attitudes shaped by this peculiarly hard discipline are more than a cast of mind—they are closer to an ethical system, in which the chief value is a particular sort of integrity—the obligation to distinguish, as far as it is philosophically possible to distinguish, between the subjective and objective parts of the experience it is examining. The chief difference between scientific and artistic modes of communication is precisely that science draws this distinction as part of its technique, while art deliberately avoids drawing it. The artist does not aim to produce beef or amplification, only pleasure (in its proper sense, which does not exclude profit). He does not assume the responsibility, if you like, of science. He can therefore communicate without scruple any sense of pattern he may have even if it is elusive and practically unimportant—after all, he is only saying 'Look!', not 'Hear ye the word of the Lord'. He can, if he likes, set out deliberately to evoke exactly that sense of significance, disturbance, or pleasure which hinders and confuses the soft-centred scientist vis-à-vis his material, or which handicaps the schizophrenic. It is his object to communicate them for their own sake, for the experiences and sensations they evoke— he can do so without any obligation of analysis and without producing any intellectual confusion—provided that he and his audience are not soft-centred to the point of no return, so that they mistake his aim and rush on-stage to kill the villain with real knives. The mathematician seems to bridge the gap between the two modes of communication very neatly. The relationships which he examines are significant, but caught by fishing in his mind. They can be precisely stated: yet, in spite of the common idea that 'two and two are four' is the hardest-centred of all possible statements, he is not bound by the realistic obligation of science—only by rules of his own making. He can create logical geometries for his own satisfaction, as the artist creates pattern and affect, without having to choose between their appropriatenesses to concrete situations, since he sets them in the form 'if (x), then (y), (z)'. In the contexts where it applies, this is ideal. It is also free of the charge of uselessness which ants level at artistic grasshoppers. The pattern which Pythagoras saw intuitively, and which links the vibrating string, the pitch of sound, and the behaviour of ripples and light, is expressible in such a way: into this pattern, set down as an equation, all processes which resemble wave motion can be fitted, and wherever such an equation applies we can expect, though we shall not always find, a whole range of further effects analogous to harmonic generation, resonance, capacitance and so on. For those who have the right endowment, this is a perfect, if limited, solution to the problem of hard- and soft-centredness.

It is also quite unlike the situation of art. However much the mathematician may be amusing himself by studying the mathematical properties of his own nervous system, he communicates his findings in a notation designed to be as unambiguous as possible. Philosophers envy him its low noise level. Artists, particularly in societies like ours which make them individualists without social function, spend most of their time producing structure which is a form of communication, but which is intentionally and highly ambiguous. They cannot verbalise its content, for even if they know what they have put in, they could not know what other people will take out—the content of the message will be different in emphasis, if not in substance, for every observer, and different again in a hundred years' time. A work of art is an information-containing object of a quite extraordinary kind—how extraordinary, a biologist may possibly realise more easily than an artist. It is more like a virus particle than a message: it may, but need not, have an explicit surface meaning, but it can produce extravagant effects in the individual minds of its audience, disproportionate to this meaning, by exploiting information already there; it continues to generate fresh positive entropy indefinitely, for its significance goes on growing or operating, as long as language and culture develop, and long after it is out of the initiator's hands. Much of the communicated matter he can neither predict nor be aware of, any more than he can consciously analyse everything which went into it. This quality of direct interference with the mind and still more the mood of the recipient is art's unique property as communication—it can communicate empathy directly—in Bachofen's phrase, it 'imparts awareness where language can do no more than explain'.

Communication-theory is the fashion of the present; the number of times that these things have been said before according to the fashions of the past must run into six or seven figures.

I have said them again chiefly to put them in my own terms. When I was six, Dr. Richards was settling the problem of soft- and hard-centredness in art. At that time I used to distinguish, as my son did later, between real stories and pretend stories. Dr. Richards[2] distinguished between pseudo-statements—pretend statements, that is—and real statements. Those who find the artist soft-centred when he talks about God or Prometheus are really being silly, for these are only pretend statements, which we need to employ in poetry because they have sentimental associations. Of course he does not mean them, or at least he ought not to mean them—any more than he would love his girl if her neck really resembled a swan's, or give his eyes for a good drink. A priest who objected to the pantheistic unorthodoxy he found in Wordsworth's

> . . . still communion that transcends
> The imperfect offices of prayer and praise

was simply being literal-minded.[3] Everyone knows that artists think with a soft ball: whether Wordsworth meant what he said or not should not matter. In fact (though not in this precise context)

> The long-established and much-encouraged habit of giving to emotive utterances—whether pseudo-statements simple, or looser and larger wholes taken as saying something figuratively—the kind of assent we give to established facts has, for most people debilitated a wide range of their responses. They are so used to having their responses propped up by beliefs, however vague, that when these shadowy supports are removed they are no longer able to respond. Over whole tracts of natural emotional response we are today like a bed of dahlias whose sticks have been removed.[4]

There is a sense in which this is true. Unfortunately, while the response natural to literary critics and professors of English is not visible externally, or at most involves a change of sedentary posture, another form of natural response may be action, and it was this which was evoked by the pseudo-statements of, for example, D'Annunzio and Nietzsche, with consequences which would probably have dismayed their authors.

Artists have opinions. They formulate hypotheses because one cannot live without doing so. They may express and believe

11

them—or they may express, without knowing it, what are in fact half-baked or ill-conceived hypotheses, and retreat, when challenged, as theologians do, saying that they were speaking not in a literal but a Pickwickian sense. Their work, while it may indeed be figurative and nobly ambiguous, does not exclude the ordinary lowbrow type of meaning which we find in letters, newspapers and scientific journals. An artist, unless he is an imbecile, must therefore in some matters be a thinker, like his fellow men; and if he is a thinker he must think. He must recognise hard-centred matters, and know that they call for hard-centred treatment.

There is no real difficulty over the 'figurative simple'—nobody takes the Ode to a Skylark for ornithology. Nor is there necessarily any difficulty in appreciating an artistic effect when it is supported by concrete opinions with which we disagree, provided these opinions are not contemptible in themselves: *The Wreck of the Deutschland* moves Protestants and atheists, unless they are monumental bigots; what is moving about it is not Hopkins' Catholicism, but the obvious sincerity of his own emotion, and his power of making us feel as he did. Indeed, it would offend us only if he had been enthusing about pseudo-statements—if, that is, his religious emotion had been gammon. Not that I would consider Catholicism a hard-centred opinion; but it is an opinion, not a figure of speech, and recognised by Hopkins as a matter for belief and argument.

This is the recognition which I think we are entitled to demand from the artist when he states or assumes or expresses that which is important and might be taken seriously. It is splendid to communicate empathy—but at times empathy breaks heads. In Julian Huxley's words, 'we are not really free to believe nonsense, even when nonsensical beliefs involve no immediate or obvious practical consequences—a belief . . . is always in some degree operative or effective: it always tends to issue in action of some sort.'[5] Fantasy is the artist's prerogative, but if he makes pseudo-statements about his solvency he goes to jail, and the court will not be impressed if he tells them his false cheques were really poems of a highly original kind. A good many writers who took a purely figurative smack at the Jews or expressed the wholly symbolic glories of conquest have tried to do precisely this, in our lifetime; such extreme cases of mischief only illustrate the general fact that ideas are ideomotor, whether we express them in earnest or not: indeed, because of his powers of exploiting the irrational directly, they are more dangerous in an artist's hands than in a preacher's.

People have long been debating how much intellectual irresponsibility can be tolerated in art. This is surely the wrong question, an understandable product of the tradition of artistic shamanism, or of the superstition that there is a hopeless incompatibility between thinking and feeling. Both the Inquisition and the Marxists on one hand, and Dr. Richards' essay on the other, seem to me to be missing the point—that different kinds of statement, whether they call themselves art or science, impose different standards of integrity, and it is the character of the matter which decides. Individualist art such as we have today calls for an extremely sharp awareness, on the artist's part, of the exact intellectual level at which he is working. He shares the general human responsibility for the consequences of his thinking, magnified by the fact of public expression.

I want to illustrate this by example. W. B. Yeats adopted in his poetry an elaborate mystical cosmology—better suited, at first sight, to describing the movements of nucleic acid molecules than those of history. There is a recurrent, cyclical pattern in events. Alternate half-cycles are opposite in sense (Christ is followed by Antichrist)—they also contain a secondary spiral, on the model of a bobbin in a spinning-jenny (pern), each unwinding the thread its predecessor has wound, moving in increasing circles ('a widening gyre') until it reaches an escape-velocity and 'flies apart', but simultaneously winding its own thread for the next half-cycle to unwind. The frame time base of this process, if I may call it that, is the platonic *annus magnus*, set by Yeats at 26,000 years. The strobe time base of 'gyres' depends on the phases of the moon. Each recurrence of history has identifiable landmarks—reversed in sense, of course, in each half-cycle—the Divine Child of one cycle is Helen of Troy, of the next Christ, and of that which is impending a 'rough beast'. Fuller development of this scheme, which it has taken much scholarship to sort out, would need Dr. Henn's[6] diagram and table. It applies, moreover, not only to history but to ontogeny, for the individual is winding and unwinding a self and an anti-self on a scaled-down model of the same kind.

We may be inclined to cry 'Stop, stop!' long before this point. And yet we recognise this intellectually exasperating pattern. It was on the wallpaper of our own nursery. It is the pattern produced by the human mind 'ticking over'. Soft-centred is a weak term for such a construction; but it is not much more so than Milton's cosmology, which was theologically respectable, up to a point, when he adopted it: it is less original than Blake's, which was all his own work, and, incidentally, particularly interesting for his independent invention of something strikingly like Hinduism. Yeats' system is by contrast a compilation, built up like a stamp-collection from voracious, uncritical reading. The ingredients are the contents of Harpo's pockets—Ayurvedic astrology, numerology, Plato and Spengler, physics and mathematics, *choses vues* like the bobbin—which was, I think, the starting-point, for somewhere in childhood Yeats was deeply impressed by it—archetypal symbols, private grudges, reactionary politics, Celtic mythology: hermetic, syncretist—poetic, in fact, in the popular sense of being pretentious nonsense grandly expressed. At the same time, the familiar nursery-wall face looks out of it, and we cannot help according it a gesture of recognition.

If Wordsworth did not really believe that the sense of uplift on a country walk was more spiritually exhilarating than the imperfect offices of prayer and praise, Yeats could hardly believe all this. But because it is the same shape as the 'zero input display' of the human mind, it is a brilliantly successful armature to support the poetry. If it is pseudo-statement, no more, and if Yeats is amusing himself with astrology and magic, why worry? Only because this was apparently not Yeats' own estimate of it. It may have begun like that—but by the time he wrote *On the Boiler*, when the recurrence of history led him into some bizarre political attitudes, he is taking at least some part of it seriously, as a guide to action.

For pseudo-statement or not, this theory is trespassing. It would upset the Russians, and rightly. It has got out of the sphere of waking dream, into the sphere where hard-centred criteria apply, where questions will be asked and the answers will matter. 'History repeats itself' is a wholly-permissible platitude. 'Each age unwinds the skein wound by the last' is a more original platitude; statements like this, with enough ideas behind them to be more than whims, are the usual intellectual pretext of lyrical poems other than love poems—the poem grows by embroidering them. Neither is profound or important. But 'History is cyclical—it repeats itself in detail without directional progress—it can be predicted on a long-term basis, for the cycle has identifiable landmarks' is a proposition of quite another order. It is not a myth, a conceit or an emblem, but a theory—on its way here to becoming a delusion. The cyclical recurrence of history is a hard-centred matter. If it were true it would be highly important, as Yeats himself saw. It provokes not a poem but an investigation. By insisting on its reality, as no Hindu would dream of doing, Yeats has confused as well as excited himself—one can imagine circumstances in which such a miscalculation could have done actual harm to his fellow men.

I chose Yeats in preference to an agitatorially didactic writer—Shaw, for instance—because in his case it happens that we can trace much of the process of confusion between fact and fancy back to the sense of significance which I mentioned. Yeats had a unique mental endowment in his capacity for waking dreams. If the gyres were an error of judgment, his discoveries in symbolism were quite another matter. His growing excitement at finding the images which occurred to him spontaneously in these dreams echoed elsewhere—in magic, astrology, myths and his wife's automatic writing—was the exact reverse of the excitement of the Surrealists when they rifled psychoanalysis for symbolic material. We can understand the impression such correspondences made on him; they were Crusoe's footprint. The link between his own mind and the Mind of the World became clearer at each fresh discovery.

The risks of such a situation are familiar enough if we know the history of pseudo-sciences like pyramidology, which grow into *idées fixes* by selecting coincidences. But in this case Yeats was quite justified in taking his intuitions for intellectual discoveries: that is exactly what they were. He had a unique power of detecting intuitively the 'preferred patterns' of human symbolic thinking. His explorations were to a large extent anticipating Jung. But he had no criteria to determine what the significant matter signified, and it was the intensity of conviction implanted by these discoveries which upset him. They were

> 'Self-born, high-born and solitary truths
> Those terrible, implacable straight lines
> Drawn through the wandering, vegetative dream.'

He could neither explain them away nor leave them as intuitions. If the idea of endless recurrence which he found outcropping repeatedly in his own mind was echoed again and again elsewhere, it must represent not only a repeated human conviction but the secret truth about history: an excited search of the record produced, as it always does in such circumstances, passable confirmation. He had discovered a non-rational short cut to enlightenment. We can watch the original sense of pattern growing into a soft-centred hypothesis. At the same time, all this pattern-tracing activity and the conviction that went with it were a diversion from having to face less biddable matter, which was latent in the dream material, and against which it protected him after the common fashion of dreams.

What matters most, for our argument, is that the ideological business matters so little. If we have not the key, *A Vision* is deeply obscure, though here and there in it the pattern can be sensed if not seen, and without it '*The Second Coming*' and passages in other poems will not mean to us exactly what they meant to the author. But this is true of *Hamlet,* or for that matter, *Hiawatha*: the bulk of Yeats, even when it follows the blueprint, still has clear and evident meaning. Yeats' symbolic, soft-centred intuition was so accurate that the half-hearted structure of theory which he set up to fulfil the duty of thinking need never have been verbalised: it only served to mislead him, and it does not greatly help us. It is more important, in reading the poems, to know the events of his life, because they are not common property and we cannot guess them or sense them intuitively—the pictures he had seen, which Dr. Henn has identified: Maud Gonne as Helen, daughter of Leda and of the white Leitrim swans, stolen by MacBride to set Dublin on fire: Maud herself as Leda and her daughter as Helen, coming to set fire to the ageing Faustus and his tower: the struggle he had with age and impotence; the Sligo landscape. These matter more than the Great Mind—they form the 'manifest' content of the fabulous dream.

Milton's cosmology is an irritation which all but school-children under compulsion jump over, to keep up with the current of the verse. It is so with Yeats—what he regarded as substance is for us barely scaffolding. Since the material itself is illogical on the pattern of dreams, and its associations do not progress in rational straight lines, it can only be accurately communicated by suggestion. Blake tried to expound similar ideas, and only succeeded in making the expository poems unreadable. Yeats is saved by his sensitivity to symbolic associations and his integrity in presenting them. In the event he communicates not only images and the emotions they caused in him, but a sense of their latent content as well—experiences into which the poet had no insight, and insight about matters which would have been in-tolerably painful to him. In fact, the whole philosophical part of the system appears, at last, not simply as wanton pseudo-state-ment, gammon for gammon's sake, but as the protection erected by a deeply sensitive mind against the self-knowledge contained, or disguised, in the poems.

Yeats is the best modern instance of the splendours and miseries of 'pseudo-statement' and of soft-centredness. I have taken him because his miscalculation in one type of statement is so gross and his success in the other so complete. He fully shows the problem which artists, particularly Romantic artists (on whom their art makes greater, not lesser, intellectual demands than others, for they are didactic as part of their brief) face in relating art to thought. They may be, and sometimes must be, soft-centred. Awareness of the 'Great Mind' is part of their profes-sional equipment. But they should, also as part of their pro-fessional equipment, preferably be capable like the rest of us of the discipline of hard-centred thinking. Above all they need a clear idea of the level of meaning at which they are working, the fiduciary limits of the ideas they express.

In view of what has been learned about the unconscious mind, this may sound a tall order; who then shall be saved? But in fact it makes no unreasonable demand on insight. It is only an ex-tension of the attitude demanded of them by their bank manager —the 'sense of reality' which is common currency, and which psychosis disturbs. Kokoschka[7] put it quite clearly: 'A fallacy is blurring the clear distinction between what is in and what is out of the mind.'

Scientists are subject to unconscious forces like others, but are still committed to clear certain small areas of their thinking as well as they can. Most artists, while observing the ordinary standard of sanity, without difficulty in ordinary matters, do not try to recognise their intellectual limits in their work, because they have been taught to believe they need not, and that it will ruin their sensitivity if they do. Minor miscalculations, it is true, will not spoil their art—only confuse their judgment. Balderdash can inspire art if it can inspire artists. Occasionally both with mystics like Yeats, who trust their belly-thoughts, and with pugnaciously didactic writers like Shaw, who are also amateur thinkers, we recognise that a particular idea is loaded, and wish they would put it down before someone is injured—while major miscalculations can easily betray an artist into a gross indecency against man, and disgust us with him as a person regardless of the merits of his technique (nobody will want to read a Fascist poet, if there is one, for some years to come).

At the other extreme, wholly hard-centred theories put into art have repeatedly miscarried without bringing down the works which contained them—Zola's genetic determinism does little to spoil his social realism today. Indeed all hard-centred ideas borrowed from science, since they are approximations and analogies, not 'truths' or even pleasant patterns, will eventually go the same way; artistic soft-centredness, which depends for its effect only on human reactions to stimuli, lasts far better than any hypothesis—it is not under the duty of constant revision as the price of being serviceable.

I think it would generally be true that in spite of all that has been written about the profundity of art, really profound or original *concepts* are very rare there. It is a perceptual rather than a conceptual medium—what we more often find is the original working-out and elaboration of commonplaces, the merit being in the manner rather than the matter, and above all in the communication of feeling. When we do meet ideas significant and difficult in their own right, ideas at the boundary of communicability, such as Wallace Stevens' recurrent preoccupations with the interaction of order within the mind and order outside it, I strongly suspect that they have been thought out 'in plain', and coded subsequently for transmission as poetry—that they have been through the hard-centred mechanism, and have been stated and un-stated again. Ideas of this kind seem to go best, too, when they are inconclusive—meditations or statements of relationship rather than ill-judged theories. One could make a far better poem out of the integral calculus than out of the Doctrine of Predestination.

If, finally, we want to see an artist fulfilling his imaginative and intellectual responsibilities properly, in spite of heavy unconscious pressures on his work, we need only look at Shelley. Nobody can now be in much doubt about the origins of his preoccupations, or the way in which they dictate his themes. He is, if anything, even better at transcribing them directly in fantasy than Yeats, for he sets up fewer barriers against their latent content. Yet for all the personality-problem behind his various enthusiasms, and his complete lack of real-life judgment over them, he never lets go. Behind every fantasy there are precise, intelligible ideas—the poetry and the neurotic fantasy secrete them like bone inside a limb. Wherever the ideas become applicable to real affairs—to politics, to ethics—they become hard-centred, a regular weightbearing structure. This is the result, simply, of intellectual discipline: Shelley, like Yeats, recognises that his own mental processes are mirrored in human behaviour, but in much more intelligent terms, for he projects them into the real problem of power and human liberty. The result is not a farcical cosmology but the growing realisation that father-hating and father-slaying, the obsessions of his own mind, are a critical part of the real machinery of tyranny and of revolutionary tyrannicide—that the neurotic myth has to be transcended in history as well as private life, and that this is the key to human freedom. This is something very far from pseudo-statements and hermetic calendars—it is a discovery of hard-centred significance, a more important intuition than those of Hamlet or Sophocles, for it is a Promethean intuition: like the intuitions of science it leads to the possibility of action. Shelley, indeed, is to Freud as Yeats is to Jung. Over a century later we can put the social significance of human psychosexual development in more exact

19

terms, and even relate it to primate behaviour generally, but we have still to realise its political implications with Shelley's vividness.

The intellectual requirement of science, then, while it is inappropriate to the making and the intention of art, is applicable to the artist's thinking—to the intellectual content of what he does, his understanding of the reasons for doing it and the way in which it is done. Though artists have long been encouraged to be obstinately soft-centred in all these matters, as proof that they are sincere, spontaneous, sensitive, and inspired, this soft-centredness appears to me no more respectable than soft-centred genetics or supernatural physics. The first effect of the prevalence of science and of scientific experience on the artist is, or ought to be, to rid him of the idea that he is doing something beyond the reach of logical analysis, which is august, divine, transcendent and significant *for that reason*. Significant and even august it may be, if he does it well, but neither divine nor transcendent. Yet many artists, even those who are otherwise sceptics, still privately think that it is so, as their predecessors believed themselves inspired by gods and muses, and depend on this idea to convince themselves that what they are doing is worthwhile. I think that in our society this hieratic notion of art, respectable as it is, and inevitable as it has been when art was social, like that of the temple-builders, is one of the more mischievous kinds of soft-centredness, for it does real harm to the character and work of writers and painters who hold it, whether it causes false humility or arrogance. A riddle or the cricket's cry is not really a fit reply to doubt, unless what we are saying is at least partly humbug, and the descendant of hieratic art is typically neither Blake nor Keats, but Bunthorne.

Knowledge of science, and still more the need to practise it, militate against the soft-centred mode of thought even if we are predisposed to it. They make us familiar with the fate of past *mystiques*; and with the idea that a process can be unanalysable, with all the pleasing characters of paradox and cross-reference and indeterminacy which make art uniquely pleasant and uniquely valuable, not because it is magic but only because it is complex. The mystique of beauty is the mystique of complexity—the mystique of good sherry. It cannot be reliably synthesised, and it may never be exhaustively analysed, except perhaps at prohibitive expense, and quite probably not even then, for our palates may remain more sensitive than our chromatographic methods. But it is not a suspension of the natural order, or a higher type of consciousness, or the abode of a deity or an entelechy. Neither is art, though it differs from sherry in being something more than a flavoured intoxicant, even in a society which has deprived it of the social functions which it once had.

In the past, the choice of art or science, presented as antipodal, and hence of a training in one or the other, has depended on the chooser's personality, and the two figures of the weather-house have been forbidden, and structurally unable, to come out together. The prestige of soft-centredness as the nobler vehicle, together with his own inclination, has often kept hard-centred thought out of the artist's way, and his person out of hard-centred company. Yeats, who was expelled by the Theosophists for demanding evidence, was unfortunate. Where Shelley drew intellectual stamina from Godwin, Yeats had only Mrs. Besant. Artistically-minded people have usually had no trouble in insulating themselves from the hard-centred technique and its attitudes. But soon, if our society goes on as it is going, those who want to avoid contact with those attitudes, and training, if only minimal, in those techniques of thought, will have to take definite evasive action. The skills of the next generation will be skills as much of thought as of action, and one will not be able to escape from them even in amateur market gardening, for they include vegetables in their sphere of application just as much as nuclear reactors, or our motives for choosing horticulture rather than physics.

This seems to me, from the viewpoint of art itself, wholly a gain. Intellect is the tenth muse, and we have been far too long ashamed of her. The artist had gained nothing and lost much from the convention that, like the devout, he must play out his thinking life with a soft ball only, and it will matter much less, by comparison, whether or not science gives him technical insights into aesthetics.

The intellectual obligations of art and science are not identical, but the intellectual obligations of artists and scientists do not differ from those of non-artists and non-scientists in social behaviour and their 'engagement' in the life of the species: they are only more conspicuous. A combined growth of hard-centred thinking and sensitivity to our general humanness is something which we must now all cultivate if we are to control our rulers and remain alive. We have a vast capacity for the irrational. The practice of science does not make us proof against it. It can barely maintain true hard-centredness over the course of one concrete problem. But it has its effect. An inefficient mode of contraception does not guarantee any one person against maternity, but it can still materially reduce the fertility rate; this is the effect of the scientific habit of mind upon the birth-rate of irrational ideas. It permits the artist, who must both use and control the irrational, to plan his intellectual family. If he already knows how to feel, the prevalence of science is likely to help him to think.

II

Darwin and Freud

An potuisset Natura commodius alibi viri genitale
collocare; et cur unum tantum, non duo, ediderit?

IOH. BENEDICTUS SINIBALDUS: *Geneanthropeia, sive
de hominis generatione decateuchon.* 1642

TWICE in a century, the human self-estimate has been
rudely upset by the work of one man. A hundred years ago
Charles Darwin showed us that we are not unique, and
before the turn of the century Sigmund Freud had showed us
that we have no insight into our own motives. Darwin and Freud
are the two caryatids who support the structure of hard-centred
thinking about man by man, and their work forms an essential
unity, intellectual and scientific. Freud has the greater effect on
our understanding of behaviour, aesthetic behaviour in particular,
but Darwin provides the groundwork for the understanding of
Freud. We had better, therefore, take them together.

Darwin's *Origin of Species* had its centenary last year. It has taken
the whole of that century for its implications to leaven the mass of
general sciences—they are just beginning to penetrate into the
most resistant fragment of all to biologically fundamental ideas,
the practice of medicine. Freud's principal discoveries have been
published just on half as long. They originated in medicine, as a
by-product of the search for a method of treatment. They have
spread luxuriantly in the social sciences, and partly because of this
luxuriance they are only just beginning to penetrate biology at all.

In fact, in putting Freud and Darwin on the same footing, I still

23

need, I know, to appease, if not convince, colleagues in all the sciences, including psychology. General scientists have treated Freud rather as the Americans have treated the Communist Chinese—by mixing a morose hostility with the public pretence that he is not there. I think this foreign policy—in relation to Freud, that is—is almost certain to change, and I think it is important for human biology that it should.

I cannot, I think you will realise, go satisfactorily here into the problem of putting Freudian and Darwinian ideas on an equal basis of acceptability. Verification in psychoanalysis has its own special difficulties: these have just been discussed at length in a published symposium between psychoanalysts and philosophers, with a minimum of mutual comprehension.[8] The Freudians would have got much further and fared better if they had talked to biologists instead; they would have found less need to resist the idea that Freud's hypotheses and methods are in some way scientifically as well as conversationally indecent.

Both Darwin's and Freud's hypotheses were developed to explain empirical observations—both are in some particulars almost certainly wrong; both have been strikingly successful in organising facts which were known but not understood when the theories appeared, and facts which have been discovered since, which Darwin and Freud cannot have known. Both come within the ordinary scope of scientific method. If we want to correct the man who thinks that Darwin discovered monkey ancestors and Freud discovered sex, we shall tell him that Darwin discovered natural selection (the idea of evolution was not new) and that Freud discovered the unconscious mind and infantile sexuality. So far there would be pretty general agreement that these are experimentally investigable and proper hypotheses. When we compare Darwin's account of the probable origin of Man with Freud's account of the origin of individual behaviour, we are still dealing with meaningful and important suggestions, but here the criterion from physics, 'no hypothesis which does not generate an experiment', is inappropriate—it applies in fact rather better to Freud than to Darwin; we can, with suitable training, repeat Freud's observations—anthropogenesis, like history, is inherently unrepeatable by experiment.

We should not be put into any philosophical perplexity by

this—we ought now to be used, at least in biology, to hypotheses which are not like physical laws, but more like Michael Ventris' reading of the Linear B script—the test of them is how far they give consistent translations of empirical fact when we take proper precautions against circular fallacies of the Shakespeare cypher—Great Pyramid type. Darwin's use of this method of inference in applying evolution to man is a model of how it should be done.

After a hundred years, with a few powerfully motivated exceptions, most people now accept the main drift of Darwin's argument. After fifty years, if we take the essentials of Freud—infantile sexuality, the Oedipal reactions, dream-symbolism, defence mechanisms and repression—some people will say, like Pasteur, 'Mon Dieu, sommes-nous encore là?' and others will angrily deny that any of them are verifiable at all. I have a feeling that this is not very different from the situation of Darwinian anthropogenesis, perhaps not fifty, but certainly twenty years after the *Origin*.

Someone has said that the best argument for Freud is that he makes intelligible sense of *Tristram Shandy*. I find that quite a cogent argument, and no doubt our grandfathers, if they were not morphologists, were less convinced by Darwin's vast collection of examples than by the fact that he made intelligible sense of the contents of the British Museum. In 'selling' Freud to the general scientist, the most telling evidence may well be the goodness of fit to matters of common knowledge, rather than specialised information from clinical interviews, which is the real source of the hypotheses. Biologists know that doctors are notoriously bad exponents of scientific method: the evidence from clinical analysis, which is most impressive when one sees it, is obtained under conditions which they can neither experience easily nor control. For the artist and the palaeontologist the experience of the *argumentum ad Tristram Shandy* is much the same. After Freud, after Darwin, neither can think in quite the same way again; their professional experience is set in intelligible order, and if the pattern is not in detail correct, they cannot help recognising that something very like it must be. They are right to be suspicious of it—but if Freud's hypotheses can be shown to create as much intelligible order elsewhere, and especially in their own fields as

25

did Darwin's, both may demilitarise their off-shore islands and suggest experiments to see if the hypotheses are true.

Penetration of science in this way takes time—one has to wait for new evidence, for tempers to cool, and for ineducable experts to die: we know that Darwin until recently excited, and Freud still excites, the worst possible emotions in both opponents and proponents. We know also that psychoanalysis is a special case in that we are probably dealing with matter which is uniquely able to upset our judgment. It is a problem in scientific argument which is new, quantitatively if not qualitatively, because we have to recognise the fact of so-called 'resistance', which we can easily verify in our own experience, and which makes it as hard for some people to consider the relevant ideas as it would be for them to see into their own ears; and, at the same time, we have to refrain from using this as an argument on theoretical questions, because it is obviously the Joker to end all rational discussion.

Let us now try to fit Darwin and Freud together and see what the speculative structure looks like.

Darwin published the *Descent of Man* in 1871—thirteen years after the *Origin*. The whole of the evolutionary argument except the explicit application to man was really present in the earlier book. The full title of the new work was *The Descent of Man, and selection in relation to sex*; the second part of the title actually accounts for more than half the text. It deals with a matter which, although Darwin does relate it to man, is not a primary argument in his theory of human origins. It was something arising out of his general evolutionary theory which had been criticised, and this second book provided an opportunity to deal with it at greater length. The juxtaposition of sexual selection and human descent seems therefore to have been a matter of convenience rather than relationship.

The first and third sections of the *Descent* deal directly with the origins of man. We read the book now, of course, with hindsight, and much of the argument for human evolution is familiar. In these days of biology books by eloquent Jesuits it is perhaps the part which dates more which we can read with greatest profit—the argument about the evolution of the 'higher' faculties and the human sense of values.

Darwin and Freud

Darwin starts by answering a rhetorical question of Kant's:

> Duty, wondrous thought! that workest neither by fond insinuation, by flattery, nor by any threat . . . before whom all appetites are dumb, however secretly they rebel—whence thy original?[9]

This question Kant is about to answer himself in soft-centred terms, when Darwin answers it in hard:

> I find it in a high degree probable that any animal whatever, endowed with well-marked social instincts, the parental and filial affections here included, would inevitably acquire a moral sense or conscience as soon as its intellectual powers became as well, or nearly as well, developed as in man.[10]

Not that they would have the same moral sense, of course—if we were intelligent worker bees we should think it a sacred duty to kill our brothers, and mothers would be violating natural law if they made no attempt to do away with their fertile daughters—a horrid idea. But all social animals display what is functionally 'ethical' behaviour: presumably it is an evolved adaptation—human morality is our evolved adaptation, and Miss Cobb, who was writing in the *Theological Review*[11] that Darwinism would sound the death-knell of the virtue of mankind, really need not have worried.

The same must be true of aesthetic behaviour. Many animals show it: presumably, since it is not there to please God or amuse us, it has a function—the discussion of sexual selection suggests what, in origin at least, that function may be. The male bird-of-paradise appears to please the female by having coloured feathers—'as women everywhere deck themselves with these plumes, the beauty of such ornaments cannot be disputed . . . judging from the hideous ornaments, the equally hideous music, admired by most savages, it might be urged that their aesthetic faculty was not so highly developed as in certain animals—for instance, in birds.'

If the aesthetic sense is a derivate of sexuality and sexual display, the moral sense must be a derivate of family pattern. Darwin gets into a certain amount of logistic trouble over the way in which natural selection could favour altruism, but this leads him eventually to the important idea of indirect selection—that an adaptation may be selected because it favours the survival of the group.

27

It pays the species for parent and child to love each other—'with respect to the origins of the parental and filial affections, we know not the steps by which they have been gained; but we may infer that it has been to a large extent through sexual selection.'[12] The 'unusual opposite', hatred and rivalry between parent and child, fortunately need not trouble us in man. We can hurry on to the inspiring fact that even earwigs of some, though not all, species show mother-love.

Finally, 'How so many strange superstitions have arisen throughout the world we know not, nor can we tell how some real and great crimes such as incest have come to be held in abhorrence (which is not however quite universal) by the lowest savages.' Because it is not quite universal 'we may reject the belief, lately insisted on by some writers, that the abhorrence of incest is due to our possessing a special God-implanted conscience.' [13] In spite of Kant, it is not built in.

One of the privileges of hindsight is that we can see how Darwin and Freud handle one another's material but skirt round one another's interpretations of it. Darwin is here relating morals to family-situation, and reaches as it were the edge of the super-ego concept. In the same way, he relates aesthetics to sexuality. But much more striking, of course, to a Freudian hindsight is the accident which sets this sort of argument side by side with the discussion of sexual dimorphism. I have not the cheek to suggest that Darwin was unconsciously aware of a relationship between them (if he had been he would have been much more likely to avoid the subject altogether) but the fact remains that we now read as a unified argument something which the author intended to take in two little-connected subjects. When in the last section Darwin does apply sexual selection to Man, he puts the Freudian coping stone on the edifice in discussing female adornment; he quotes a savage chief explaining why his womenfolk stretch their upper lips to the size of dinner-plates:

> They are the only beautiful things women have; men have beards, women have none. What kind of person would she be without it? She would not be a woman at all, with a mouth like a man but no beard.[14]

This is like one of those films where hero and heroine tragically miss one another in opposite sides of a swing door. The Freudian reader can hardly sit still for wanting to prompt him. Darwin in fact tries in the *Descent* to explain the significance of sexual dimorphism in general, but Freud, having spotted its significance in Man, explains the application of Darwin's selectionist argument to human socioethical behaviour, the point which Darwin was looking for and misses by inches.

The question of sex differences arises for Darwin in the following way. His great fundamental discovery was the idea of natural selection. It followed from this idea that any well-marked trend or development in form was likely to be in some way adaptive. In working this out, he had to explain the fact that in some animal species, cock and hen for example, there is a striking difference between the sexes—sometimes an exorbitant one, like the clumsy, two-foot-long tail of the male quetzal, which can barely fly in mating plumage: in others, like gulls or penguins, the sexes appear identical. Why did selection favour these differences and in some species only? This was an agonising problem—at one time it threatened the whole theory; we find Darwin writing to a friend that 'the sight of a peacock feather made him feel sick'.

However, it was resolved in the end. Darwin's explanation was two-pronged. Some of the instances represent different functions in upbringing—if men must work and women must weep, or rather suckle, one would expect this to be reflected anatomically. Others, like the peacock's tail and the stag's antlers, it was reasonable to explain as a means of competition between males by which the most vigorous would have the most progeny—either through ability to attract females and keep them attracted, or through the ability to fight rivals and monopolise the most desirable mates.

Darwin is inclined to emphasise this kind of sexual selection, for competitive virtues, in man. The large differences in human preferences between ages and between cultures he puts down to custom and to assortation—like preferring like. He mentions the human tendency to exaggerate physical attributes artificially—missing, in the process, the much more biologically-extraordinary plasticity of sexual object in man, the fact that the sex drive can be diverted to inanimate objects, members of the same sex, or an exaggerated characteristic, often to the exclusion of mating.

Darwin's view of sexual ornament, then, is that it is chiefly competitive. But since his time interest has shifted to another, related function of sexual dimorphism—its use in recognition. In territory-keeping birds, the cock drives off other cocks—often without actually fighting them—by displaying his markings and song against theirs. There are occasional violent encounters, but as a rule territories tend to subsist automatically by a form of behavioural agreement, based on the use of these signal mechanisms. In gulls, which do not have visibly different sexes, the signal is the adoption of a particular threat posture.[15] The cock bird defending his territory takes up a threat posture—if the intruder is also a cock, he will retaliate or retreat, but a hen will carry out an appeasement display, taking up a posture as different as possible from the threat position.

This meets the need to distinguish a potential, or an accepted, mate or mates from an intruder. The other tolerated parties on a territory are the young. These are usually protected from being driven away prematurely by the fact that the behaviour or markings which trigger the aggressive response of the parents do not appear until sexual maturity. This is necessary in species where parental dependence goes on until the young are as big as the adults. In other species, there are different precautions to keep the young away from an aggressive parent. Although brown bears are commonly monogamous, cubs never see their father, and are not deserted by the mother until they are big enough to climb out of his reach.[16] Young male Northern fur seals[17] live with the cows until shortly after spermatogenesis begins, when they go off alone and do not return until they have grown enough muscle to take place in the dominance-order of males. In general, the existence of a long-term family-situation in pair-mating animals involves two requirements—that other sexually active individuals should be driven away, either from a territory or from the female, and that the young and the accepted mate should not.

It was Freud himself[18] who wrote that there had been three great blows to human self-esteem—Copernicus, Darwin, and the discovery of the Unconscious: he attributed this final blow to Schopenhauer, but in a letter to Karl Abraham he admits that he had put Schopenhauer in the foreground to avoid having to give up an interesting line of thought through false modesty.[19]

Freud had actually, I think, very little Darwinian background.

His only obvious debt to Darwin is the idea of a primal horde in which the strongest male ruled, but it was an important debt, because it started him with a firmly Darwinian idea that sexual dimorphism was primarily competitive. He did not, however, really apply the selectionist argument to his central and most surprising finding—the nature of the anxiety behind the human fear of incest, an anxiety which appears in many respects to have dominated human social development, the so-called castration fear. This was an empirical observation which he had great difficulty in explaining—and, as Darwin had to invent the idea of pangenesis because he had not seen the work of Mendel, Freud was obliged to turn to racial memory to account for something which makes sense in evolutionary terms but in virtually no others.

Freud found that in his patients conscious behaviour, normal and abnormal, was influenced by thought-patterns which were unconscious and followed characteristic non-rational sequences; much of the content of these was sexual, and appeared to date from early childhood, and there was an extremely powerful block to making the original significance of this imagery conscious. The imagery itself showed an extraordinary preoccupation with the external genitalia, with fantasies of incest, and with fantasies of castration. This system of unconscious imagery and associated anxieties Freud called the Oedipus complex—after the Greek hero who inadvertently killed his father, married his mother, and blinded—or castrated—himself in expiation. It appeared to date from a particular period in childhood, between the ages of four and six, and the associations behind it were remarkably consistent, one of the chief components being intense anxiety over the difference between the sexes, combined, in the male child, with a fear of injury to his own genitalia. The female organs were a particular focus of this anxiety—they seemed to be interpreted as a wound or mutilation which was in itself threatening—the male child apparently saw them as a threat of castration, while the female child came to think of herself as actually deprived of a male organ.

Freud was as impressed as we are by the oddity of this at first sight, but once he had recognised the irrational train of thought behind it, it became obvious that there were echoes of it all over human behaviour, custom and literature. This becomes even more striking once we get used to the peculiar kind of non-conceptual association which determines unconscious imagery. The outburst of anxiety appeared to be connected with another mechanism which Freud had been obliged to postulate—the sexual attraction of the male child to its mother, and its resentment toward, and fear of reprisals from, the father.

Given the existence of infantile sexuality, which was perhaps the most biologically surprising part of the story, it seemed quite reasonable that the sexual object for a male child should be the mother, and that the father should be felt as a rival. But where did the fear of castration come from? It was important, because it seemed to be the driving-force behind the whole of incest-anxiety, and behind the adult behaviour-disorders Freud was investigating.

Freud at first attributed it to injudicious threats from parents, and wondered whether he might not himself be suggesting it to adults inadvertently during treatment. But it became clear that where there had been threats these only aggravated a fear already present, which seemed to appear spontaneously at the appropriate age—it was found in children who had never been threatened, children who had no parents, and in places where the psychoanalyst could not have possibly put it—from *Tristram Shandy* to the impolite ballad,[20] which gave us the phrase 'pull Devil, pull baker', where the whole business, even down to the interpretation of the vulva as a castrating wound, is turned to triumphant mockery.

There are two obvious biological comments at this point. Both have already been made by a psychoanalyst, Fenichel.[21] The first is that the Oedipal responses not only have every appearance of being in some way 'built in', but look very like a temporary organ with a function. In fact this, and the recognition that they *are* built in, are the only way of making them intelligible. (They need not, incidentally, be manifest and detectable in everyone for this to be true.)

The second biological comment is that sexuality, in its biological as well as its conversational sense, is a correlate of reproduction, and accordingly the mention of infantile sexuality at once calls for some explanation of what sexuality is doing in infancy. Some infant animals show minor sexual reflexes, such as erectility, but the occurrence of well-developed sexual drives in infancy would be an example of what is called anticipation, and this kind of shift makes one look for a possible adaptation of an old mechanism to a new function.

Freud did in fact recognise them as being built in. The tendency of his time would have been to label them 'instinctive', but this Freud would not do; not, curiously enough, because of the extreme difficulty of justifying alleged human instincts, and the uncertainty how much any built-in response owes to shared experience, but because he had throughout life[22] a fixed idea that there could be two human instincts and two only—the two posts were held by different candidates at different points in his career, but at that time both were occupied. Instead he turned to the idea of racial memory. The castration fear and the associated anxieties were inappropriate to the childhood situation in any known human society, but they might not always have been. They could be intimations of fiercer sexual selection in the primal horde, where the sons had to kill their father to possess his wives, but having rudimentary ethical qualms, as Darwin said they must, they had bequeathed them to their descendants. We find him wondering if there were ever a time when the father really castrated his sons, or whether the threat was enough.[23]

I wonder if there is an echo here of Darwin's fratricidal bees. The racial memory idea is semi-Darwinian but non-Mendelian—it is the mental equivalent of pangenesis without reference to selection.

If human sexuality had in fact been brought forward into pre-reproductive life, and had acquired a new place in behavioural development, the Oedipal reactions with their peculiar genital content could be part of this shift, or the result of it. Is there any other peculiarity of human development which makes anticipation likely? In fact there is (see graph). The curve of human growth and development differs conspicuously from that of nonprimates, such as the sheep, in having a long lag-period inserted into it between the fifth and the ninth years. The development which in other mammals is continuous is divided in man into two: an early phase, which is isolated from sexual maturity by the whole length of childhood, and a pre-reproductive phase which

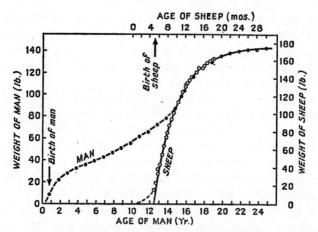

coincides with the beginning of puberty and the appearance of secondary sex characters. The two peaks of psychosexual development in Freud's timetable therefore fit accurately over two periods of maximum growth and developmental rate, which were presumably once continuous but are now separated by the lag—and by the Freudian latency period.[24]

It has been realised before[25] that 'castration anxiety', which has every appearance of fulfilling a special function, but which seems inappropriate in its present position, would be much less so if it occurred in an animal which had no lag-period; it could then represent an adaptation which protected immature males over the awkward age between sexing and achieving competitive size. If there was no lag-period in man, puberty would be complete about the age of nine. The timing of the Oedipal reactions (four–six years) would therefore still put them well ahead of the probable age of appearance of secondary sex characters; more recent workers have put them if anything earlier still. But Freudian experience has always insisted that the onset of 'castration anxiety' is in some way triggered by the recognition of the genitalia themselves. This is possibly an important clue to its origins. The timing and content of the reaction in man would be intelligible if it evolved originally (*a*) among pair-mating animals, (*b*) with prolonged and lengthening maternal dependence, (*c*) where instead of the secondary sex characters the genitalia themselves had recently become the primary sex signals, so that males became competitive long before they were mature. This might happen as a by-product of quite unconnected changes (in posture or hair density, for example) or even of an interference between growing intelligence, which associated male genitalia with male secondary sex characters, and instinct, which excited hostility to them. It would call for a major adaptation in behaviour to maintain the family-pattern, if young males had to love their mother in order to stay with her, but avoid her as a sex object, so as not to be chased off the territory. Avoidance of the sexually displaying female as a 'castration threat', and mixed feelings toward the adult male in which his genitalia served as a dominance-signal, could serve to keep young males out of the competitive situation while still maternally dependent.

An explanation of this kind can be manipulated to include most of the peculiarities of human psychosexual imagery as described by psychoanalysis, including its remarkable concentration on phallic and vulvar symbolism to the exclusion of other sex characters. It is also probably wrong. We cannot confirm it by direct observation in animals, for none of Man's direct ancestors are available for study, and modern apes may differ from us precisely in their failure to evolve such a mechanism. On the other hand, if this guess is wrong, I strongly suspect that something very like it is right. Whatever its original function, some mechanism in primate evolution has first divided our psychosexual development into two halves, of which the first is educative and morphogenetic, not reproductive; and then planted on top of any existing hominid instincts and behaviour a mechanism of character-development which involves a violent reversal of sex-responses.

There is one other reason which might lead us to surmise that the pattern of human psychosexual development is the product of an adaptation to a biological emergency—its most surprising and un-Darwinian vagueness of aim. Fixity of sexual object, at least to the extent of mating with a potentially fertile female and with nothing else, would seem to be the behavioural minimum to be expected in a system where 'fitness' is a correlate, simply, of total fertile progeny, and the nadir of unfitness is inability or unwillingness to breed. But the human sexual object is not fixed—under present conditions at least, it is rather easily displaced.

Almost all such displacements reduce their possessor's reproductive effectiveness, and many prevent mating altogether. According to Freud, the liability to these deviations is a direct hazard of the Oedipal processes, and of the need, effectively, to reverse or overcome the avoidance of the female before adult reproduction becomes possible. The miscarriage of this process—the connection is whether causal or correlative does not here matter—appears to be able to divert the sexual drive away from its proper target and dissipate it on an irrelevant one—a member of the same sex, an inappropriate part of the body, a circumstance or an inanimate object:

> Some Symetry the Foot hath with that Part
> Which thou dost seek, and is thy map for that,
> Lovely enough to stop, but not stay at. . . .[26]

the fetishist does, however, stay there, to avoid the revival of the anxiety associated with going further. The disability of the compulsive homosexual is not due to the presence of homosexual impulses, which are general in mammals, but to the suppression of heterosexual impulse by a similar mechanism.

There is more, in all probability, to the biology of paraphilias than this (one was recently excised by operation, along with an epileptogenic focus)[27] but they set essentially the same evolutionary problem whatever their cause. The human pattern of development carries, empirically, a sizeable risk of interference with eventual mating. There is a strong temptation to look for the compensating evolutionary 'advantage'. This is an instance of what Professor Haldane once called Pangloss's Theorem. If everything is for the best in the best of selectionist worlds, the peculiar mode of human sexual development must involve some overriding gain to the species—if not, it would have disappeared—or at least become reliable. This is as unsound as most *a posteriori* argument—natural selection responds; it does not plan, though when equilibria shift it will compensate. The psychosexual pattern in man looks very much like the end-product of one of these oscillations—the castration-fear is not sex-limited; instead, it is developed in the female into a rather cumbersome mechanism of 'cryptandric' behaviour (this is the Freudian explanation of Darwin's lip-stretching natives) by which the male is assisted, as it were, in reversing his responses and reaching the adult pattern. The non-teleological untidiness of this seems typical of the evolutionary 'Demon' making do. At the same time there is this much validity in the Panglossian argument, that where a homoeo-static swing of this kind opens a new possibility, selection may exploit and expand it. The Oedipal responses may carry an in-herent risk of interference with eventual reproduction, but their persistence in spite of functional ambiguities, and apparently long after the situation which produced them, may well be due to having acquired a new adaptive function in their new situation, as the feathers which evolved to control the body temperature of reptiles enabled their descendants to fly. It seems quite reasonable to suggest that this function is morphogenetic, and that they have been positively selected because of their effects on human social and intellectual behaviour.

We have still not explained why to some people Oedipal anxieties give no more trouble than the tadpole's tail does to the frog, while to others, exposed to apparently similar childhood influences, they are a lifelong handicap. Kallmann[28] has found that identical twins are more like in their liability to disturbances of sex behaviour, as in every other investigated respect, than are fraternal twins. This means very little, but there may, and some would say there must, be some 'constitutional' factors behind such behaviour disorders, even if the same factors produced opposite results in two different social settings. Consideration of this in Darwin's terms has led Hutchinson[29] to make an important suggestion—the first I have mentioned here which is directly open to experiment. If any hereditary factor regularly predisposed to paraphilia severe enough to block reproduction, there should be heavy selection against it. Hutchinson has attempted to guess what kind of physical trait might have this effect, and asks whether the differences between normal and abnormal psychosexual development may not depend on individual differences of develop-mental rate.

There are in fact, as we have seen, strong phylogenetic reasons for associating rate-determining mechanisms with the way in which human sexuality has evolved—it arises, apparently, from allometry in the early scale of growth/time. Freud associates paraphilias with a derangement of processes which occur near

37

the start of the lag-period and at a point in the growth curve where, owing to its shape, a small change in contributing rates might produce a very large change in the duration of a 'temporary organ', by moving it, like the bubble in the spirit level, along the entire extent of the 'plateau'.[30] A difference of rate, heritable or otherwise, which displaced the Oedipal behaviour by six months in an animal whose curve was continuous might shift it in man by several years, and make it persist throughout the whole of the lag-phase—during which, presumably, attitudes and behavioural patterns are hardening.

Hutchinson's original suggestion is not based on this particular consideration, and he is more concerned with the reasons which might prevent constitutional determinants of paraphilias from being eliminated by selection. They might behave like the extremes of intelligence, for which Penrose[31] suggested a system based on heterosis—they might, especially if they operate primarily through rate differences, represent multiple homozygotes of genes which persist in the population through the greater fitness of their heterozygotes, being, in other words, special cases of low vigour. Apart from the fact that the real existence of 'constitutional' factors in paraphilias has yet to be established, I prefer to heed the warnings given in Professor P. B. Medawar's recent Reith Lecture[32] about this argument and about genetical speculation generally. The Panglossian, of course, will forge right ahead—if overdominance will not do, Darwin's concept of indirect selection is ready to hand. Both intelligence and paraphilia are possible factors in social development: perhaps the need for repression enlarged the brain—perhaps it gave us a differentiated ego and therefore conceptual thought—or did the prehuman community benefit from its unusually-motivated members, and from the sublimatory expression of their drives? After all, Freud suggests that the Oedipal reactions have behavioural effects far wider than the production of paraphilias—Darwin and Freud, like the rest of us, owe their unusual insights partly to their psychosexual histories: Man, Pangloss would say, when we can catch him, may owe his reason to repression and his present existence to the advice which aim-inhibited palaeolithic geniuses gave to their normal but uninspired colleagues.

Environmental effects on psychosexual development are usually discussed in terms of traumatic experience, with much less attention to the additional possibility of direct physical retardation. Greenacre[33] found that the early traumatic experience in paraphilias was often an illness between the second and fourth year. Illness and separation from parents may indeed be physical stresses, but, particularly in children, where emotion itself affects appetite, they produce physical checking as well. The effects of such checks to growth in size in young humans and animals are usually made good by the 'post-inhibitory growth rebound', but this may not restore complete isometry, or deal with any discrepancies which have arisen in psychical development.

This idea, like most of what I have written here, belongs to common-room conversation rather than established knowledge. The trouble is that we seem to lack a common-room, or any other daily contact, which would bring working biologists and working psychoanalysts into proximity, or even collision. Nobody would deny, I think, that since Freud psychoanalytic theory has sometimes become etiolated through lack of contact with general science, while general science has never come to terms with the far-reaching consequences of psychoanalysis if only in exposing the way in which mental processes can affect observation and reasoning. I have not discussed the work of Freud's successors— partly to preserve the one-to-one comparison with Darwin, but also because Freud is still almost alone in his choice of biologically manageable categories—of scientific thinking, in other words. Jung, for example, constantly produces ideas which cry out for neuroanatomical and evolutionary statement, but his formulations have a way of being gnomic rather than operational—like the statement that the feminine of 'dog' is 'cat': we see the point, but this is not really the way to treat it intellectually. The marriage of psychoanalysis and biology is long overdue and likely to be fertile, and each has a great deal to teach the other. If between us we were able to ensure the full development of all adults, in a world which seems to call increasingly for adult minds, rather than aggregates of reaction-formations, we should certainly effect a change in human affairs which would be truly evolutionary in Darwin's sense, and justify his confidence in human reason.

I am primarily concerned here, however, with another marriage, between science, including both biology and psychology, and aesthetics—or at least between biology and art. The speculations I have been discussing in biological terms already cover almost the whole of human behaviour, because the peculiar pattern of our psychosexual and physical development is the chief element in fixing the specifically human character. The Oedipal reversal involved the need to divide our mind into compartments, albeit far from watertight, and to keep the contents of those compartments actively separated; the behaviour which evolved to stop primitive hominids from fighting their parents has made us able to think, vulnerable to symbolism, prone to anxieties of which we do not know the nature, and liable to a compulsion to express them concretely. For the moment I only want to suggest that this could account for the odd aesthetic balance in man between what seem to be simple pattern-making responses to rhythms, colours, and harmonic relationships, and the elaborate, anxiety-filled and overwhelmingly sexual symbolism which has been planted on top of them—at what stage in primate phylogeny is not clear. Sexual symbolism is not all-explaining so much as omnipresent— primitive initiation ceremonies, for example, are almost all built from impulses connected with the human concern over male-female difference and parent-child avoidance, but they are used for widely different social purposes in different cultures. The components of the Oedipal anxiety are part of Man, like his habit of walking upright, and once they are put into words they make intelligible not only *Tristram Shandy* but a great deal of odd behaviour in art, as elsewhere, which past generations have taken for granted.

Let me take one example. The most respectable and the most naturally attractive pictorial subject in European art is the naked human body. Its apotheosis is the naked woman: the psycho-somatic effects of figure-representations and sexual stimuli in art differ markedly, in our culture at least, between the sexes. Much art is a pretext for her, and there are many artists whose vocation comes wholly from a conscious wish for the privilege of painting her. In a civilisation which has compulsorily covered everyone else's nakedness, her popularity has still been successfully rational-ised as mythology, allegory, the love of Pure Form, philhellenism —even piety. The artist has by a vigorous propaganda established himself, like the cameraman and the eunuch, without losing his respectability, as the traditionally licensed *voyeur*—which is no mean feat. He defeated Victorianism by appealing to culture. He even defeated the Inquisition by painting his naked lady into an admonitory allegory of vice. Yet by tradition he may not paint all of her: until very recently he had either to conceal what he saw by the clumsiest of artifices, or falsify it by omission. Why?

This is by all standards an odd situation, and until Freud described the 'releaser' effects of sexual dimorphism an unintelligible one. A Martian biologist could not avoid asking questions about it—nor, one would think, could an intelligent artist, who normally ignored the conventions in his sketchbook. Although he could not offer a biological interpretation, he was at least aware that nakedness is magical and significant, that for some reason tensions other than the purely reflex erotic responses are set up by it, and contribute to the effect of his pictures, that decency and prudery have tended to ebb and flow over a series of isotherms of affective temperature drawn round the female genitalia, and that in most cultures representational art has been produced by men rather than women. He may have been aware that in other traditions where the naked woman is an equally 'significant' figure in art the conventions are reversed, and the artist expected to emphasise what he is expected in our culture to hide. He may even have known that in Chinese art over a long period the point of highest emotional temperature was shifted from the pubic region to the naked foot, which must be concealed at all costs; and so on through the whole range of psychosymbolic phenomena.

All this behaviour now has explicit meaning. The biological pattern behind it is not the whole of art: that biological pattern has generated social pattern, which in turn has undergone indefinite expansion in all manner of directions significant for human behaviour. There is, in other words, 'more to it than that'.

At the same time, the explicit meaning is there. Previous generations of artists have sensed it in soft-centred terms. The present generation is the first to have the opportunity of understanding it, in the sense that they can begin to state it in a hard-centred manner, even though they are not all aware of it yet, and a major book on the nude in art[34] can still be written without one single reference to this particular set of human reactions. But they very soon will be.

What matters is not the correctness of this particular set of speculations, but the fact that it is pitched in a key, and discusses human origins and behaviour, in a manner which was impossible a century ago, but is now inevitable.

Quite apart from this particular example, the professional concern of art with 'releaser' mechanisms and the human figure, artists are currently inheriting, like the rest of us, the major consequence of Darwin, Freud and hard-centredness to all human thinking—the objective consideration of man by himself. This is something which has the force of a new, Darwinian adaptation, not in the pre-human system of mutation-variation-selection, but in the speeded-up, Lamarckian system of pseudo-inheritance which developed with the power of communication and has followed the human 'break-through' in primate development. There is no dodging this objectivity, other than by decease —conceptual thought has given us science, but the accessory consequences of the same psychosexual pattern have given us the neurotic behaviour which is employing science in projects which threaten human survival. Man's ability to apply his mind to the hard-centred control of mind may prove in our time to be the supreme example of an adaptation making possible the survival of a species, and the artist cannot avoid the by-products of so fundamental a change. But it is fundamental, and particularly so for him. We should next consider the effects which such knowledge is likely to have on his art—and, indeed, on the idea of art itself.

III

Phoebus and Pan

Literature and psychoanalysis ... are similar in this respect, that it is the essence of both to represent the opposition between two principles ..., the reality principle and the pleasure principle.

     LIONEL TRILLING: *Freud and the Crisis of our Culture*

Happy people never make fantasies—only unhappy ones.

     SIGMUND FREUD: *The Relation of the Poet to Day-dreaming*

ONE reason for the tradition of soft-centredness in aesthetics, the hostility of some cultured people to science in general, and to experimental studies of art in particular, is plainly fear. They fear that analysis will interfere with appreciation, and possibly with creation as well: that understanding will tamper with our scale of values and also, with rather more justice, they fear the artistic equivalent of synthetic sherry.

There may be people whose appetite can be spoiled by knowledge, as there are others who can be confused by it, though in fact most attempts to 'teach appreciation' assume that in approaching art the more we know the better. And with one exception the actual matter of science has not so far had any radical influence on appreciation, or has had a favourable influence: the spectroscope did not spoil our enjoyment of colour, and if it were to be shown that the pleasure of proportion is connected with our balancing mechanism, or the universal attraction of Jung's mandala-patterns with the way in which the retina is projected on the brain, it is hard to see why we should enjoy them less for knowing it.

43

It must be obvious from what I have said that this knowledge has a unique relation to taste because it radically alters the artist's sense of the significance of the ideas which occur to him, the sense of significance which is the starting point of most creative work. We are coming to be able to understand our imagination. This effect does not depend upon extensive study, but simply on the fact that it is virtually impossible for anyone who has ever encountered Freudian or post-Freudian ideas, even in a garbled form, ever to approach a work of art in quite the same spirit again, just as it is impossible for anyone who has encountered Darwin to view man as his ancestors did. This is part of a general change in the human self-estimate, art criticism apart, but the artist is particularly affected, for a whole section of his experience of creation, appreciation and value is brought under intellectual scrutiny and acquires intelligible meaning.

We have to consider whether this particular kind of know-ledge, which, though it reduces his self-confidence, can ultimately only improve the performance of the hard-centred thinker in avoiding subjective biases, may not have a unique and devaluing effect on art. The initial effects—a boom in automatic painting and writing, pseudoanalytical criticism written at the level of teacup reading by entirely ignorant people, and the novelty of playing tunes on alarming symbolic material—are the least important of these consequences. There is no more risk of successfully synthetic art than of convincingly synthetic sherry. It is of the nature of the process involved that the artist cannot in fact attain complete insight into his own work, any more than he can see into his own ears, and that no work can be 'interpreted' with any reliability out of its context or without detailed knowledge of its author. The important effects of psychoanalytical knowledge—or more correctly, the knowledge that psychoanalysis exists, even without further theoretical details, for few artists are critically informed about it—will be those which follow a change in our creative sense of significance.

In our culture most if not all works of art have their origin in compelling ideas—situational, verbal, formal, symbolic—which occur to the artist's mind. The distinguishing mark of these ideas is that they seem significant out of proportion to the rational scale of values, and that they produce at the same time emotion

44

and a desire to develop them. This experience, which used to be called inspiration, is the basic unit, as it were, of the individualistic art of modern societies—it is the answer to the question which is sometimes asked, whether the artist intends or aims to communicate, whether he has an audience in mind. In the initial experience he presumably has not, though he may immediately think of one. If the sense-of-significance component is strong, he may have an overwhelming desire to communicate it, and rationalise the significance as a judgment of value (truth, beauty, revelation and so on) in the process. There are, of course, plenty of other motives for the production of the materials we classify as art—for a start, their production is, with us, an occupation. But there is general and traditional agreement, both among artists and among critics, that this particular combination of experiences —sense-of-significance, cathexis, desire to develop the outcropping theme—is a uniquely effective motive.

Psychoanalysis revalues this experience because it modifies the value we attach to this sense of significance. If we know that some or all of what we paint and write has an expressible 'meaning' which accounts for the emotion it causes us, we shall want to know what it means (unless our resistance is too strong, or our fear of the deflation of traditional values too great—in which case we shall quite possibly deny the interpretation, suppress the work, or go on calling it 'numinous' for fear of finding out). Some 'significant' ideas are so because they resonate with patterns in which human non-rational thinking tends to be contained. These patterns, Jung's 'archetypes', cannot be 'interpreted' as such, because they have no specific content—they can only be stated; and art has long been concerned with the business of stating them. They are 'forms without content, representing merely the possibility of a certain kind of perception and action'[37] —grooves in the mind into which our perceptions and imaginings fall with a positive sensation of 'rightness', and down which, unless we control them, they run with increasing momentum. The direction of such 'archetypal' grooves can be seen by giving them content, as we use smoke to demonstrate draughts. Vast amounts of human mental energy have been diverted into following them, because of the sense of significance associated with them. They are the chief enemy of scientific, but the chief vehicle of artistic, thinking. It is difficult to see in what respect those which appear overtly in art and mythology can be called unconscious: it would be more correct to call them inarticulate.

Freud's biological interpretation unites the content of these patterns as a glove unites the individual fingers—not only does it make sense of *Tristram Shandy*, it makes sense of the emotional impact of this 'significant' content, and of so much else that we should need strong evidence to exchange it for uplifting generalities. Artists are not called to make technical judgments as between theories, but in general they will usually find that Jung's archetypes verbalise thought patterns which they already recognise occupationally, while Freud's interpretations fit their motive content and explain it, as far as it is explicable. This is not a scientific synthesis: it looks biologically plausible, however—the archetypes are an unhomogenous collection of trends or sequences in non-rational thinking, some of which may reflect neuro-anatomy and others linguistic habits or common experience: those which are ingrained, 'museum specimens from past phylogeny', in Jung's own terms, may be of very different phylogenetic ages and at very different levels of brain organisation, and the peculiar development of sexuality which seems to have been a key change in human evolution may well be superimposed on them. Thus the mandala pattern, which imitates the teichopsia figures of a migraine aura, may well owe its appeal directly to brain structure—the sexual symbolism which is so often associated with it appears to be the outcome of processes in human mental development and the peculiar significance of genital imagery which goes with them. I will be returning to this particular subject later.

At the personal level Jung's metaphysics and Freud's icono-clastic rationalism, which are upsetting to the scientist and the artist respectively, represent a classical soft-hard antithesis. This might be more depressing for intelligent artists if they were not occupationally more receptive than anyone, except possibly evolutionary biologists, to the idea that human aesthetic and social behaviour is a phylogenetic development of sexuality, which they can identify in their own experience of cathectic ideas without having to overcome their resistance to complete inter-pretation. The psychoanalysis which 'revalues' art-making is therefore overwhelmingly Freudian analysis. The perception of 'archetypal' significance is a satisfying or an intoxicating experience, rather than a disturbing one, when it occurs in the course of composition. The disturbing feature of 'inspiration' is not the intuition of pattern but the intuition of content, and of active resistance to a latent but struggling, and at the same time threatening, content. Analysis offers to translate this significance from emotive to explicit terms. Symbolism in one's own and others' work, once this possibility is known, presents an intellectual or even a moral challenge rather than a conviction of insight —emotion is replaced by interest or by anxiety. Moreover the explicit biological 'meaning' behind cathectic ideas, baldly stated, is limited in amount and nearly all of it quite irrelevant to conscious adult behaviour. Knowing its probable nature does not decrease its power to excite us personally, and we cannot as a rule interpret it unaided, but knowledge might reduce our sensation that it is significant as a starting-point for art.

I say 'might be' because I never met an artist for whom it was so, though there are probably very disturbed people whose resistance to interpretation is so great that the mere possibility would silence them. The fear of devaluation chiefly affects the sensitive critic, who sees the risk of a blighting outbreak of scientism on the human imagination. Unearthing the biology behind the mind-process 'involves reduction of the symbol to its origins, and once the symbol is in this way dissolved, it is of no aesthetic significance. . . . One might as well admit that the impossibility of avoiding such a translation is a serious defect in the psychological critic; for him the naïve acceptance (of Blake's poem, *I saw a chapel all of gold*) is impossible—here at least there is no beauty without mystery.'[38] One might call this—the reduction of the symbol to its origins—the characteristic revolutionary process of our time. If we aim to abolish our naïve acceptance of the irrational—and this, I take it, is the object of psychoanalysis—we must accept the loss of a naïve approach to poetry. But I would question this in Sir Herbert Read's own experience when he wrote, for knowing the probable Freudian origin of this sequence of symbols, he still enjoyed the poem—while I enjoy it more for understanding what gave rise to it, and Read's later essay on Shelley[39] suggests that he has come to the same conclusion. It is

47

hard to see why such knowledge should be more deflating than the knowledge that this object is carved in maplewood or that that one is made by applying oil-paint to canvas, which can only spoil appetite and palate if we are quite lacking in a sense of proportion and relevance.

These are old and unnecessary qualms; they really spring from the soft-centred unwillingness to recognise that art is made by and for men, and can be expected to bear human thumb-prints—we value it for, not in spite of, its roots in our neural and psycho-sexual development, and to object to a work because one can uncover these roots in it is like objecting to a picture because it was painted with a hand made of skin, bone and muscle; or to one's mother because she was a mammal. A more important and much more substantial question is the relation of art to pathology. Pearls and oak-apples are aesthetically pleasing manifestations of something wrong with their hosts. Many works of what we call art seem to resemble them. Medical psychology has proved enormously instructive in understanding individual artists, their motives and their line of development. It is now, in spite of all protests, an element in appreciation which is here to stay. Understanding of the oyster's discomfort does not reduce our interest in the pearl, but we are consumers: if the oyster recognised the irritant tapeworm larva for what it was, he would at least not call it an inspiration, and, though he would have to make a pearl, he might not make such a large one. A pearl, moreover, is marketable in spite of its origin—a revelation is not. If St. Paul had attributed his vision by the roadside to its probable cause—heatstroke, perhaps, or minor epilepsy, or a sharp attack of an infection—it would have remained an alarming and impressive experience, but it would not have made him a Christian Saint and apostle, still less a martyr.

It is important for us to decide to which of these—oyster or saint—the artist is really analogous, because their activities are different in outcome, and any revaluation of motives will affect them differently. The oyster, if it had a sense of beauty, might equally well complete the pearl for its own sake even if it recognised a tapeworm larva as its original motive: and the pearl would be worth something. The saint could not possibly complete his mission for its own sake if he realised that it arose not from an inspiration but from a seizure. Granted, in other words, that most people are unconsciously motivated in their choice of occupation, if all of them were suddenly endowed with complete self-knowledge, some would undoubtedly be able to go on with what they were doing—not for the motive which set them at it, but because it is worthwhile in itself: *secundum artem,* 'the superego approves the sublimation'. Others would not. Some occupations exclude insight. One could become a doctor to satisfy childish sexual curiosity, but go on being a doctor with full insight—one could not (I suggest) go on being a nun. Can one go on being an artist? Or more accurately, granted the present place of art as an amenity, if nothing more, will humanity go on needing or valuing it in the presence of hard-centred insight into the means and the matter of it? Certainly they want it now, because the scientific background of that insight is barely rudimentary, and art is, and has been, a major source of data to increase it. But a Philistine could argue that they may have to be weaned from it in the interest of hard-centredness. There is even the alarming possibility that it might ultimately come to stand in the way of insight—to be, like religion or ideology, one of the enlightenment-professing defence-mechanisms to which humanity attaches itself to avoid the need for rational self-knowledge, and at times a positive threat to public health.

In less alarmist terms, psychoanalysis raises the question of the pathology of art as a criterion in aesthetics, and could raise the question in some minds of its general worthwhileness. Art-production is a human activity so general that, like toolmaking, it has the look of an adaptive skill—one with social functions, perhaps a means to make individual variation congruent with human social habits, or to deal with inacceptable consequences of our unique use of childhood sexuality in forming adult behaviour. It may even be the transducer 'intended' by the evolutionary Demon to play, for the social consequences they produce, some of the 'archetypal' discs which selection appears to have built into our mental equipment. These are all entertaining speculations, and where art is a social activity, taking its place along with rituals, dances and purposive group activities such as hunting, something of the sort might well be true.

But our art is not now a social activity in any such sense—it is a highly specialised, individual activity, and some parts of it are grossly swollen. To alter it we would need to alter society. Psychoanalysis is likely to make us look harder at the functions and effects of the kind of art which we know—the kind about which Freud, though not Jung, is chiefly talking—a private activity which, in our society, is often practised by rather disturbed people, and which may be becoming the prerogative of such people. We can properly ask what it does in its new setting, if it does the artist good, if it does others good, whether it is still comparable to the art of *ur*-social man or whether it is something different.

Neither hard- nor soft-centred schools of psychoanalysis are fully satisfying on any of these questions. Freud's view is brief and to the point, and a sharp comment on the art and the artists which he personally encountered in practice, whose work is less analogous to an organ than to a tumour.

> (The artist) is one who is urged on by instinctive needs which are too clamorous; he longs to attain to honour, power, riches, fame, and the love of woman—but he lacks the means of achieving these gratifications. So, like any other with an unsatisfied longing, he turns away from reality, and transfers all his interest, and all his libido too, on the creation of his wishes in the life of fantasy.[40]

Originally it is the fantasy which is his consolation, and it is for private consumption, but if he is talented he will polish and develop it for its own sake: if he is both talented and lucky, the resulting object will appeal to others besides himself—all the more, no doubt, because the fantasy which it expresses chimes with theirs, saying with brilliance what they are unwilling or unable to say for themselves—'and then he has won, through his fantasy, what before he could only win *in* fantasy—honour, power and the love of woman': he will be not only fed but famous.

The uncompromising tone of this is typical of Freud. He seems to be on the point of adding (it would be perfectly true) that talented neurotics are fully aware of this possibility, and that after its immediate origin as fantasy the next main motive of the individualistic art which our culture produces is prestige-creation for the artist, however much he may say about its spiritual significance and about the joy of creation. People devoid of talent who wish to become professional artists far outnumber, in our society, those in whom natural talent proves irrepressible. Art is accepted as a justification both for fantasy and for eccentricity of private conduct, it is a profession, and the role of artist is one which is deliberately chosen. Being an artist is itself a fantasy, like being a hero: it is also a role which appears to select particular fantasies—scoptophilia in painters, for example, or travestism in dress designers. But it is not unique in this, for all other actively-chosen roles in society from hangmen to professional politicians, presumably recruit their personnel in the same way. Scientists are no less likely to select themselves for the fantasy-possibilities which they know will be accorded them in our folklore—it is a problem in medical education to keep such personally-involved candidates out of psychiatry, at least until they have some insight into their involvement. The same is true of volunteers in the social sciences.

Jung's version is equally typical of the man:

The wholeness and the healthiness of the creative function is seen in the murky light of neurosis, which is of course an undoubted product of repression in many cases. In this way creativity becomes indistinguishable from morbidity, and the creative individual immediately suspects himself of some kind of illness, while the neurotic has lately begun to believe that his neurosis is an art, or at least a source of art. These would-be artists, however, develop one characteristic symptom: they one and all shun psychology like the plague, because they are terrified that this monster will gobble up their so-called artistic ability. As if a whole army of psychologists could do anything against the power of a god! True productivity is a spring that can never be stopped up. Is there any trickery on earth which could have prevented Mozart or Beethoven from creating? Creative power is mightier than its possessor. If it is not so it is . . . an endearing talent, but no more. If on the other hand it is a neurosis, it often takes only a word or a look for the illusion to go up in smoke . . . for all this psychology is to blame. I should be delighted if a knowledge of psychology did . . . put an end to the neuroticism which makes contemporary art such an unenjoyable problem. Disease has never yet fostered creative work; on the contrary, it is the most formidable obstacle to creation . . . . The unconscious is the ever-creative mother of Consciousness.[41]

By the end of the paragraph which begins with this last

sentence, consciousness has come to equal creative significance. If we can get over the bewildering mixture of agreement and irritation which Jung's Wagnerian manner generates, we will see that there is matter here. He says, if I may presume to translate the libretto, (1) Freud has grossly overstated his case in making an unceremonious equation between art and neurosis, (2) many artists are certainly neurotic today, but many are bad artists, (3) that creativity is a natural function, (4) of which he does not understand the exact significance, though it fills him with enthusiasm. Jung distinguishes art in general human culture, in other words, from art-as-we-have-got-it; a valid distinction which his deification of the creative impulse only confuses. Elsewhere he has made it clear that in his opinion art-making has a *vis medicatrix* of its own which does not depend simply upon the discharge of anxiety in fantasy, but on the filling of irrational pattern-making impulses which are highly mischievous if they erupt to satisfy themselves at the expense of our everyday behaviour or our public beliefs. This is a much more interesting idea, though it is one about which we have very little evidence. The apotropic and psychotherapeutic uses of art have only just begun to be investigated. We know that it can work in this way, though not precisely how.

> With the advance of reason, we have lost the main historic content of the collective mind: the symbols of religion are no longer effective because they are no longer unconscious. We still retain structural features of the mind that cry for definite satisfaction . . . will the psychologist unite with the critic to define and solve this problem.[42]

Some at least of the 'structural features of mind' (Read's expression is a much better term than 'archetypes') which bias our behaviour in this society are like the conduct disorders we might expect if we tried to bring bees up individually—they are adapted to a different setting. At the same time, I think that Jung's view, coupled as it is with his rather evident mysticism, could bear fruit other than those Read intends. The matter of hard-centred and soft-centred fields of activity, which I discussed in comparing art with science, takes its origin here. It is at first sight attractive to see the world's discontents as the hunger of atavistic needs demanding some kind of inspiring, harmless or demulcent content, and to look to art to provide it—with the object of giving them something which does not matter to worry, so that they will not bite that which does. The unconscious is the source of many of our mental energies: yet it seems odd to deify mental patterns which Jung himself traces back to lower levels of mammalian psychology. One mystique has gone, so let us replace it with another—Yeats instead of Aquinas. If the symbols of religion have ceased to be effective because they and their metabolic pathways have become conscious, that would appear to me to be an inevitable end, indeed, an excellent thing. Art has some of the characters of a cultural vitamin. There can be a synthesis between nutrition and cooking, as there is between eating and pleasure—but not between nutrition and absinthe, and soft-centred procedure in the fields which have once come under hard-centred scrutiny is the absinthe of the human mind: Jung's breath sometimes smells strongly of it. Even if it were true that Freudian psychoanalysis made art impossible, we should still have to prefer psychoanalysis with reason to art without it.

Fortunately we do not have to choose—in this case Jung is undoubtedly right; the two are compatible and, indeed, complementary. Nevertheless, the majority of the art of our present society comes into the category which both Freud and Jung identified as neurotic in origin, whatever may have been true of the Lascaux cave painters. According to Freud, those who make individualist art in compound, urban cultures differ from the neurotic—the person whose living is handicapped by attachment to unreal and irrational attitudes which he cannot modify—only because, unlike him, they make their fantasies and preoccupations concrete, as 'works'. This art, in other words, is characteristically produced by people who are lacking in insight over a deeply significant part of their conduct: nuns rather than oysters. Others have gone much further—Bergler[43] writes that he has never met a 'normal' writer, that those he has encountered are typically driven by a pathological grudge, and that only seriously disturbed people in our culture have any inclination to produce literature. Honest introspection, and a look at literary friends, is enough to wither any writer's inclination to reply to such statements with insult—they are very probably true. They seem also to imply that if such disturbed people had had adequate insight they too would have had no motive to produce art at all—except perhaps as a quiet and repetitive geometrical activity: art at least would have none of the tusks and scales, the empathy, the infatuation and the *scènes de tragédie* which our culture associates with the name. We might like it, as we like flowers, but nobody could conceivably be possessed by it.

One could argue that on practical grounds it might well be better for all of us if they were not. Nietzsche described the condition of those who are so possessed as Dionysian, but Dionysians are not amiable companions unless one is equally drunk, and Nietzsche had to be put away. If we recognise—and it is the crowning achievement of hard-centredness to enable us to recognise—that what applies to science really applies to living, and that the 'confrontation' is the same in substance throughout all fields of human thinking, then the defence of Dionysian art seems to require a kind of double standard—like that which recognises that alcoholism is an evil but encourages a drinker who is known to be funny when tight. It is not, we might very well argue, Dionysus who presides over such art—his inspiration at least wears off overnight—but Pan, the god of irrational fears and sudden flight, who presides over our politics and religion, and who has so far presided deplorably over human history in general.

Irrationality is the enemy of man, as imagination is his heritage —neurosis, meaning an obstinate and ingrained irrationality which limits its owner, and which he cannot defeat, is by definition a wastage and an obstruction. It is the eternal No. If it is the substance as well as the firing-pin of art, then public health and arts are certainly enemies. This is a familiar impasse—that of aesthetic moralism. It is, in fact, quite false; psychoanalysis does not commit us to any new moralism in art (it is much more likely to liberate us from moral anxiety over the conviction, which people of taste have always held and rarely been able to defend, that 'immoral' or 'socially unedifying' works of art are often also indubitably 'great' works—we can now see why) but the new knowledge does introduce certain artistic responsibilities and critical values of its own, and these can very easily be misconstrued into a moralism of the familiar sort, which denounces this, that and the other work as 'diseased'. The effects of 'individualist' art on society are too large to discuss here, beyond saying that they are probably overrated compared with the effects of society on art. But the nature of artmaking and the demands of public health, or of clinical psychiatry, are not at loggerheads, theoretically or clinically. Neurotic and irrational motives are a clog on performance and a gross liability to the artist as to everyone else. They silence him quite as often as they inspire him; artists who can be separated from their neuroses by treatment perform better, not worse. Whether they would have had the motivation, in our society, to become artists without them cannot be shown.

Freud's basic contention is that the artist is one who cannot act out his fantasies—he can only express them as such. He differs from the neurotic in that the products engage his attention and skill, and acquire merits apart from the original motive which decided him to write a book, and not upon a wall: and from the psychotic in that 'the artist possesses his fantasy—the madman is possessed by his'.

I think we can best see the answer to some of these questions of near-critical assessment in art if we first consider the implications of psychoanalysis for scientists—the followers of the 'hard-centred' criterion. Compared with artists and critics, general scientists have so far managed to avoid these implications for their work, but psychoanalytical ideas, while they are quite certainly not all of them hard-centred, are themselves products of the hard-centred approach to human behaviour, and they radically challenge the convention of objectivity in hard-centred methods. They show that unconscious and quite irrelevant factors can determine not only the choice of hypothesis, or of science as a career, but the ability of a given observer to observe and record correctly, and the probability of unpredictable parapraxes, biases and obsessions in his work—as much among the predisposing factors which make one man able to 'see' a wholly original interpretation of the facts as among those which blinker another against the self-evident. The hard-centred constructs produced by an individual scientist are therefore quite as much a product of his personality, his childhood, and the stage which he has reached in psychosexual development, as any work of art, and they can be far more seriously affected by his idiosyncrasies.

This line of thought is unpopular, and general science, in so far as it is aware of such ideas at all, has dealt with them by putting them resolutely out of mind—helped by the intelligible but mistaken distaste of some psychoanalysts for confirmatory, and especially statistical, experiments, and the fact that the study of mind by itself, like the checking of instruments by their own readings, presents a special problem in empiricism. The resistance of artists, who are used to living with an awareness of the irrational, has been less. In fact, however, the status of art in the face of some of the new hypotheses is more, not less, equivocal than that of hard-centred activities. Neurotic motives and unconscious associations can handicap these, limit the insight of those who practice them, and vastly increase the wastage in human thinking. But because science is by *its own terms reality centred* there is a final screen which the bent material cannot get through. All science ends in what the French call a confrontation—either it squares with 'reality' and works in practice or it does not. It cannot be autistic. Irrational forces in scientists reduce the yield of science—they divert precious time and human happiness from the product into scrap—it is precisely the severity of this inspection which makes science different from all other human mental occupations. There are, of course, plenty of issues where a yes/no demonstration brutal enough to make us choose between our wishes and our sanity cannot be had. But in the long or short run 'science' faces this test or ceases to be science. 'Archetypes' apart it has the added protection against small-scale fads and individual obliquities that these differ between individuals, and the fact that we can see them in our colleagues compensates in part for the inability to see them in ourselves—they can be detected, in nine cases out of ten, by a show of hands.

The test of scientific hypothesis is not whether it springs from an irrational source, or whether the motives behind our original choice of it were neurotic and hidden motives—but whether the discipline of confrontation is able to control these motives later, when we come to compare it with fact. It does not matter in the least that Darwin or Freud or Newton owed their preoccupations to the irrelevant contents of their respective childhoods—what does matter is that many, if not most, of their hypotheses survived painstaking comparison with the real world, and that they were able to reject or remould some others which did not. Some, no doubt, but not all—we can, if we like, strike a profit-and-loss account over the others, balancing the extent to which these great originators had their vision restricted by unconscious forces against the likelihood that, without these forces, they would never had had an original idea at all. As to the hypothesis which is irrational in origin (all really original hypotheses may well be so) but which remains irrational, defending itself irrationally against confrontation with things-as-they-are, it can survive surprisingly and mischievously long in fields where there is plenty of cover, but sooner or later it will be caught and confronted; and neurotic science, however venerable and eminent, is not science —it is non-science, anti-science, and ultimately nonsense.

Freud's remarks about the artist must make us ask how far this applies to art. Sir Herbert Read has suggested that psychological study ought to be able to draw a line for us between neurotic and non-neurotic art,[45] taking as a test the 'purposive genuineness of its symbols'. This might be workable—but neurosis is a state which affects a person, not a book or canvas—it involves us in a large value judgment about mental 'normality', with all the usual terminological difficulties; and the judgments we might make in terms of 'purposive genuineness' are only doubtfully compatible with those we normally make about literary merit or pictorial ability. It is indeed possible to distinguish between the work of very neurotic people and that of others, often without much special knowledge—between Strindberg and Pinero, for example, or Edvard Munch or Goya and Sir Alfred Munnings. These are not very good instances—(Munch and Goya at least might qualify as psychotic if judged by their art alone) but they suggest that purposive genuineness is not a sufficient, if it is a necessary, aesthetic test. Is the symbolism of *Tristram Shandy* purposively genuine? Is it more or less purposively genuine than that of the martyred saints of Christian iconography? It is surely a fundamental lesson of hard-centredness (and analytical psychology) that there is no such thing as sincerity, though there is such a thing as deliberate insincerity—and that our symbolisms speak for themselves in spite of our purposes.

Freud's picture of the creative process is explanatory biologically speaking, but it is far from complete, and it is influenced by

his own rigid distinction between normal and abnormal development; having over-stated his case he seems a little concerned to
save the prestige of art by distinguishing its content from 'true'
neurotic self-deception. In this he seems to be introducing a
bifurcation of nature which his own observations do not support.
At the same time it is hard to identify a specific neurotic stimulus
in, say, geometrically-patterned pottery. It may be true that art
is a displacement activity—it may also be a built-in human propensity like fantasy or scratching. Given such a propensity, neurotics,
who have on their minds much which can be acceptably discharged only as make-believe, will embody it in art, and talented
neurotics in good art. Such art is highly characteristic of our
society, in the prevalence of various stereotypes, of rigidity and
guarding, and of death-centred and aggression-containing ideas
—so much so that in creating the illusion of novelty and originality it is the psychotic rather than the neurotic who currently has
the advantage. For us the artist is typically a shaman—one who
has acquired his power over us by virtue of having undergone, and survived, a disintegration of his personality.

Fear of a medical moralism to replace a religious has already
made both critics and artists play up the idea of such disturbed
art as an Aristotelian cathartic. There seems so far very little
psychiatric evidence for this either—least of all in the study of the
private lives of artists—and it is only doubtfully applicable to
their audiences. The nearest approach is perhaps the function
which Freud attributed to dreams—that these are not mere
emanations, but have a specific and usually beneficial place in
the economy, a definite dream-work to perform. In some senses,
whether we are makers or audience, the effect of a book or
picture is much like that of a dream. But there are important
differences—we dream with our sense of reality in abeyance,
and we dream our dreams, not other peoples'. The trouble with
art is that we absorb it awake, via the mechanisms which take
in data from the real world, and confusion is continually arising
between it and things-as-they-are. The possibility of confrontation with reality is there, and is clamant, and we are perpetually
tripping over it emotionally. Dreams cannot normally mislead us
—being endogenous, we know where we are with them: they
are only tolerated, indeed, because we know they *are* dreams. But

art, even phantasmagoric art, is such a cunning and uneasy hybrid between real and unreal, fact and wish, hard- and soft-centred matter, that we need an effort incompatible with appreciation to sort them out, and cannot do so at all where we are deeply involved. And we can choose our art, and do choose it, to minister to our preoccupations and nourish rather than correct them. Dreams, where 'we' are concerned, select themselves; but Emma Bovary's reading matter had a way of being selected to minister to her changeling-fantasy. Would she, if she were real, read her own story? And if so, how much insight would she get from it?

I suggest that the model of motivation and sincerity in art is really very like that of motivation and sincerity in science, putting 'work of art' for 'hypothesis'. Any systematic or random inequality in the mind may generate a picture or a theme, and the product will reflect the maker's preoccupations as well as those of his culture and of man in general—what matters is the subsequent development, and how far it survives the process of confrontation. This is Freud's own conclusion—that in art as against neurosis simple, *Vorlust* triggers the work but *Endlust* finishes it. We start it to relieve our anxiety and finish out of craftsmanship or for prestige—the neurotic unease is the sand-grain, and if our aesthetic vocation is sluggish in keeping us at work on the pearl beyond the minimum needed for comfort, our hope of acclamation and royalties will do instead. This is a confrontation of a sort—but of a different sort from that in science: it is much more equivocal than the censorship of hard fact. Art is a soft-centred activity—with what precisely are we confronting it? Panic-art—pseudo-Dionysian art, that is—is not reality-regarding; but by tradition art need not be so, provided we can recognise the discrepancy. On the other hand, it has not the right—and I choose the word 'right'—to be reality-falsifying.

That is the total extent of the moralism which we need to make our 'confrontation' critically useful—it is only the same discrimination which I was demanding of the artist earlier on, between the legitimately soft-centred and the illegitimate invasion of hard-centred fields—but here I am taking it a stage further than the mere ability to distinguish real from unreal which we demand of non-psychotics. It now implies a distinction most people, artists

59

included, are known to be unable to make in their daily life—at least without special treatment, and probably not always then—between their real and their apparent motives. The substance of this demand (still aesthetic, not moral—failure is evidence of bad art, not of turpitude) is that the artist should not, intentionally or unintentionally, mislead. He can produce fantasy absolute, fantasy qualified, opinion, or realism; play or earnest;—but he must not be deceiving us, or himself, by the presentation of manipulated reality.

I think this is what Sir Herbert Read had in mind when he said that the test of non-neurotic as opposed to neurotic art is the 'purposive genuineness of its symbols'. We can really only assess such criteria when we come to use them in practice and see how they apply to the natural history of actual literature or painting. The case of Yeats I have already discussed. The case of Shelley raises directly the question of the therapeutic effect of art on the artist—Shelley is the rare individual who obtains so much insight from his own work that he performs a partial self-analysis. The result of this sincerity could possibly be dangerous rather than beneficial to some—one expression of self-accusation is accident-proneness, and one cannot help noticing that Shelley, whose poems contain some notable fantasies of self-combustion, and who was haunted by an imaginary assassin *Doppelganger* armed with the poet's own pistols, was accidentally drowned at very much the point in the process where a medical analyst would have been looking out for squalls—possibly Zeus dragged Demogorgon down with him in earnest. Shelley's art was neurotic, in origin at least—at the same time it is purposively genuine as well as intellectually robust, and seems to demand the same respect, quite apart from its literary quality, as any other stout pursuit of self-knowledge.

A still better example of the equivocal character of purposive genuineness is that of Flaubert. Here the pattern is quite different. Shelley derived insight from fantasy: Flaubert is the father of naturalism—the art centred in things-as-they-are, which attempts to keep insight and fantasy separate. When I spoke of Emma Bovary reading her own life, and its possible effect on her, I spoke as if she were a real person. Her story is about the social manifestation of the neurotic incapacity for happiness, the conflict of fantasy with things-as-they-are. It is written with insight which enables us to examine her motives as though she were a real person—to speculate about her preoccupations, to decide whether her dissatisfaction reflects resentment at her peasant background and so on. Her behaviour is self-subsistent and consistent—so is her marriage, the personality of the husband who chooses her, and whom she chooses, the kind of lover she takes. One could recommend the book to a real person in her position, in the hope that she would gain insight into her discontents.

We also know that there were two Flauberts, Shem and Shaun —the one creating resplendent erotic fantasies, writing *Salammbô* under the propulsion of a 'désir lubrique sans érection', and returning time and again in spite of his friends' dissuasion to his *Temptation of St. Anthony,* an extravaganza which filled him, as the *Revolt of Islam* filled Shelley, with 'unbounded enthusiasm': the other writing *Madame Bovary* on the marital misfortunes of one of his father's medical students, at Bouilhet's suggestion, to cure himself of the Dionysian mode which had erupted in the first draft of the *Temptation*—and becoming thereby the founder of documentary naturalism.

This would seem to be a simple enough case of binary fission, one half of a great artist feeding the fires of his own preoccupations, with results which are spectacular if nothing else—the other keeping its hand on things-as-they-are, doing its duty, and producing masterpieces of naturalism in which the neurotic distortion is clinically exposed. If this were so, it would be an acceptable model for dealing with the problem of artistic motives, and purposively genuine into the bargain, for Flaubert is as frank as Shelley in his recognition that the motive of *Salammbô* is plainly and consciously erotic.

Unfortunately it will not quite do. Salammbô perishes spectacularly for having touched the veil of Tanit. But so does Emma Bovary, and it is vain for us to justify her end by saying that this was a true story. The real Mme. Delamare did ruin her husband and poison herself—but the cathetic idea and the *coup de théâtre* are there. All that has happened is that Flaubert's realism is selecting a theme to fit the fantasy which *Salammbô* and *St. Anthony* realise in the imagination. I doubt whether Flaubert really thought that he had bisected himself successfully. 'C'est avec la tête qu'on écrit', he said—'si le coeur la chauffe, tant mieux, mais il ne faut pas le dire.'[46] *Salammbô* might be a sugar plum, the fruit of a 'désir lubrique sans érection', and *Madame Bovary* a victory of reason over imagination—'il découle de ce roman un enseignement clair': but with the passing of time the boundary between comment and empathy shifts. Emma hates the world around her, not for itself but for the drabness of its contrast with her wishfulfilment—for refusing to come when called. Frédéric likewise—the lesson of his education in feeling is epitomised in the last chapter of *l'Education Sentimentale*: the world is the Turkish 'establishment' which as a boy he visited to put his fantasies to the test, but funked it at the last moment. It is intolerably drab by contrast with our fantasy—either we are disappointed, or we try like Emma to act it out regardless, with appalling consequences. Much better to run away and keep the fantasy. In fact—and it is Flaubert, not Frédéric, speaking— humanity is 'une vaste association de crétins et de canailles' which he enjoys seeing 'bafouée, déshonorée, sifflée'. It is Flaubert speaking—but by now it might equally be Emma. She is in revolt against a world which is not biddable, not like her wish. Flaubert is equally in revolt against a world which disgusts him because it is not the world of his outwardly rejected but inwardly cherished erotic dream. In his choice of subject Flaubert is indeed 'acting out' as blatantly as his case history heroine though less disastrously to anything but his own mental peace. He is Saint Anthony, and like the historical saint he is manufacturing his own demonic tempters, who are none the less terrible and not to be exorcised by common sense—not even by the insight that created Emma Bovary from a real personage, for it chose her because some of the sexual *diableries* of *Salammbô* could be acted out upon her. Yet in a sense both are realistic, for anyone who lives, in fantasy, in the *Salammbô* world commonly lives, in fact, in a world which comes to resemble Emma's or Frédéric's world. Much if not most of our own culture does so— it is not for nothing that years ahead of the cinematograph camera *Salammbô* is the first film. An artist can no more successfully bisect himself in the interest of 'purposive integrity' than he can get an unbiased idea of the sound of his own voice. Nor can we bisect him.

We can take the relationship between preoccupation and imagination a stage further if we look at the work of Blake—here we can actually see, as plausibly as we are ever likely to see, the relationship which I suggested between Freudian origin and Jungian superstructure in the process of creation. Starting with the shorter poems (*I saw a chapel all of gold, My mother groaned, my father wept* and its myrtle-tree sequel) we can follow the way in which the effect and the symbolism of submerged, biologically-generated childhood anxieties organises the whole content of the imagination round itself, as a magnet organises iron filings. The babe, the father and the mother of the lyrics become characters in a kind of gigantic family charade, titans caught up in patterns of endless recurrence, ambiguous presences with their female emanations and themselves epicene, part archetype, part emblem—a vast exploration of spontaneously generated patterns in the mind, remarkably akin in its general manner to the theogonies of the Vedas. Influences from actual mythology—Ossian, the prose Edda, Swedenborg (who may have known something about Hinduism at first hand—Blake probably did not) contribute to the detail, but much of it evidently comes straight out of Blake's head. It is certainly not unconscious, in any intelligible sense of the word, for it is written down in black and white: indeed the only unconscious thing about it, as in the myths of Yeats, is the original biological significance of the symbols and of the emotion behind them. The imaginative structure moves further and further away from these as it develops, gaining concreteness from Blake's magnificent visual imagination, and the sand-grain which set it building is buried under layer after layer of protective development, until the real father and the real baby of the simplest vision, having done the round of the archetypal grooves, reappear as a kind of fourfold Brocken spectre—vast shadows on the nursery wall.

> All, all these gyres and cubes and midnight things
> Are but a new expression of Her body.

wrote Yeats, of his own work. In Blake, they are brought back into contact with realities through the philosophical and emblematic content they acquire in the process of expansion. Since human affairs and these enormous allegories are the product of similarly-shaped nervous systems and are governed by the same preoccupations, symbol and social reality, when they meet, fit together neatly once more. The poet has rationalised his own social and artistic beliefs, and finds that his prophetic imagination justifies them. He has drawn a map of the inside of his own head which is interesting and relevant in itself—which has real intellectual significance. At the same time the product, like a primitive ceremony or a dream, is capable of carrying out a work, an emotional operation on its audience. Apart from this hidden or internal effect, it adds vastly to our understanding of literature. It is an odd reflection that Blake, who abominated Locke's philosophy from his adolescence and wrote in a mood of dedicated enthusiasm, and Sterne the Lockeian with his legpulling and his Freudian buffooneries, should have come so close: inspired prophecy and the inspired mickey have taken hands, Albion and Uncle Toby have kissed each other. Who, I wonder, was the victor in Uncle Toby's struggle with his Sakti? Did the sacrifice of his virility keep her within him, or would the Widow Wadman be able to say, as Enitharmon says to the vanquished Los

> This is Woman's World, nor needs she any
> Spectre to defend her from Man . . .
> No! I will seize thy fibres and weave
> Them, not as thou wilt but as I will . . .
> Let Man's Delight be Love, but let Woman's be Pride?

Somewhere between Blake's fourfold apocalyptic universe and Sterne's bent reality is the Dublin where Ulysses and the fourfold manifestation of Earwicker-Shem-Shaun-Finnegan fight the same ambiguous battles. Blake would have understood this convergence. In his *Island in the Moon* he had even attempted something like the Sterne manner. Sterne deals with his material, and the unease which generates it, by slapstick and the guffaw—Blake by his insistence that imagination is the true reality and reality is *maya*, Feminine illusion. Shelley the rationalist transmutes his dream imagery little by little into real terms—and in doing so comes close to interpreting it, with a dangerous strain on the insulation of his mind. Blake sees tyranny, stupidity, the sleep of Albion and the rule of Urizen, as the fruits of empiricist reason, which he treats as the enemy of imagination. Shelley attributes them, with more justice, to the lack of a reason which is also imaginative. Both are in a sense right. Both are relevant to our self-comprehension, valid as part of the range and repertoire of art. Both draw interior maps, but the travellers on these, as in Flaubert's realism or Sterne's nonsense, are the same: they still take their origin from shadows which were cast in the first place on the nursery wall.

There is one particularly instructive recent example of this relationship: in the poems and autobiography of Edwin Muir we can see the whole process in train. Muir's youth was a chapter of misery, during which he wrote nothing. In 1919, when he was thirty-two, his life was transformed in a single year by three events—happy marriage, escape from Glasgow, which he hated, and the beginning of a therapeutic analysis offered him by a medical friend. In the first weeks of this he experienced a phantasmagoric dream which he describes in the autobiography, and which is transcribed directly in two poems: *The Ballad of the Soul* and *The Fall*. Muir's dream is immediately intelligible to a psychoanalyst—it would be equally intelligible to a Tibetan adept, who would give names to the 'divinities' he encountered in it. As the analysis progresses, this material comes under control, with a great release of literary energy and of personal happiness, which lasted him the rest of his life. At the same time, in spite of the clinical success of the analysis as far as it went, he does not achieve complete 'liberation of intellect'—he remains deeply concerned to pursue the 'mystery' inherent in the symbols which still preoccupy and fascinate, but no longer disturb or silence him. I suspect that his analyst was a Jungian with a similar sense of mystery, and that a Freudian analysis, by referring the symbols to their biological origin, would have given him not Faith but insight—bubbles are still rising from the old Oedipal anxieties even at the end of his life, when he experiences a revelation-like reconciliation with his childhood religion.

In Muir's case, where we have with the poems a candid parallel account of these non-literary phenomena, several things are quite clear. Neurosis, so far from 'inspiring' poetry, prevented him from writing at all. He began to write in the process of catharsis, and continued to do so after. Nevertheless the poetry emphatically does 'originate in neurosis'—the symbolic material and the pre-occupations remain exactly the same, and the author revisits them with a continual conviction of their significance and mystical importance. The poetry seems to replace the analytical sessions—the 'dream work' serves to maintain morale. It could be written only when the neurosis itself was coming under control—prior to this, although the fantasy was available to the mind it was not accessible to literature. The soft-centred conviction of 'vision', which the poet regards as a mission and an inspiration, is in fact disabling—it prevents active literary purpose, as did Yeats' mysticism. At the last it is still a protective mechanism against insight. This, indeed, may be what poetry of this type is 'for'—it is possibly fortunate, in view of what happened to Shelley, that Muir's dream-vision took the form it did: the function of the dream is, after all, protective. But it is not a source of hidden truth and enlightenment by-passing and transcending reason—rather the reverse.

I think I have sufficiently indicated the difficulty of applying public health criteria to criticism. Plenty of artists are 'cases' and suffer from it—so does their art. If Flaubert was a 'case', it was more by reason of constitutional illness (temporal-lobe epilepsy, by all accounts) than neurosis *bien entendu*, and if we make a 'case' of Blake we shall have to call that superb visionary's symptoms aptitudes. The man and the work are indeed inseparable, but they call for different standards of valuation.

The real answer to the art versus neurosis problem in our culture, in so far as I can suggest one, may lie in the remark of Lionel Trilling which I quoted at the head of this discussion—that Literature and psychoanalysis both deal with the opposition between reality and the pleasure principle. I think it possible that art always originates, or can originate, at a point where these principles collide. It is a temporary and controlled regression which increases our grasp on the real. Art is in origin *making* (an older and better but now hopelessly trade-fallen word for it); making is the distinguishing attribute of man, and it is the common property of all made objects that they are in some way related to this collision between endogenous mental activity and the environment. A made object is a part of the not-I which I

have shaped and can to some extent control—it can be a pros-
thesis to extend my body so that I can more effectively control
things around me (in plain words a tool) or a consolation for
being unable to do so, with a blurred area between in which my
control over what I have made makes me hope that its real
counterpart will become more biddable—if I cannot catch a deer,
I can draw one which will be my deer, I can even draw myself
catching it, and the process of making the wish concrete might
possibly bring the real event closer. Or it can be a source of less
articulate pleasure—a child has never seen a green horse, but for
some reason which he cannot verbalise he would like to see one,
and makes one for himself. 'J'ai envie de voir ça', said Flaubert
of *Salammbô*. (There are, of course, plenty of more complex
categories—objects which have marked mental effects on the
maker or on other people among them, which partake of all three
modes of making.)

Science—hard-centredness—is the methodology of separating
these modes of 'making' and their mental equivalents: distinguishing tools and concepts from symbols, substitutes and fantasies.
In theory, wherever tools are effective, symbols of this non-
operational kind become unnecessary; what we become able to
do we no longer need to imagine, except by way of rehearsal. But
in fact, Freud's statement that happy people do not make fantasies
is analogous to saying that happy people, being fully in equilibrium with all that is in or outside them, do not move, for lack of
stimulus. This merely generates the conclusion that there are no
happy people. The child who draws patterns in the sand with his
toe and imagines he is an architect or a king is only 'unhappy' in
this rather technical sense, and there is art which only expresses
a discontent of this order—the reason for its rareness today is
social rather than inherent in the nature of the wish to make.

I want now to deal with quite another matter. So far I have
been assuming that the artist is both ignorant and passive—that
while he is himself a subject for analysis, and may be upset by
garbled versions of psychoanalytical theory, he will not bother to
use it as a source of information.

This, of course, is false—artists have for half a century been
making extensive use of psychoanalytical matter, both as an
iconographic quarry—a public imagery to replace or supplement

or contain the older classical and Christian iconographies—and as a source of understanding of the place of art in general.

Synthetic sherry, as made by the surrealists, actually presents the simplest case of this influence. There have been three main surreal techniques, none of them new—the presentation of equivocal objects and odd associations which set the anxieties of their audience in motion, directed Rohrschach blots; the attempt to re-create dreams and fantasies by free-associating; and straight-forward construction, taking symbols and concepts out of the book. The resulting vintage is not very good—so poor as to dispel most anxieties about its effect on the market—largely, I think, through a misunderstanding about the accessibility of 'unconscious' material to its owner. Automatic painting or writing does not automatically produce images of universal human import. Most of it seems to reflect undigested matter in the immediate 'pre-conscious', partly *choses vues* private to the maker's recent experience, and partly material from deeper levels which has already been rendered respectable enough by censor-ship to be admitted to consciousness. This mixture cannot be 'interpreted' like a horoscope or tealeaves, and has little or no 'universal' significance. Where classical and recognisable Freudian themes appear in surreal paintings and can be 'interpreted' pat, they have generally got there out of the book, and are accordingly no longer symbolic but emblematic. Artists who select such themes will probably also reflect their preoccupations in their choice, but they are most likely, I would have thought, to do so in the themes they leave out. Here once again it is the psychotic artist, whose mental insulation is faulty, who is at an advantage in apparent originality and in the alarming character of what he produces.

I do not see why the synthetic—or emblematic—use of ideas drawn from psychoanalysis should be more aesthetically objection-able than the synthetic use of ideas drawn from Marxism, physics, or Christianity. They cannot be used to work the oracle and make bad work artificially exciting—or more accurately they cannot be used more successfully in this way than our own sense of box-office. Jung's systematisation of the images contained in myth-ology is not new to the artist—he has taken them previously, as Blake did, from the myths themselves and from his own intuitions of 'significance', and if he uses Jung as weak poets use Roget's Thesaurus he is only shifting his iconographic source a point closer to anthropology and a point further from introspection; while Freudian concepts actually orientate his art-making activities in the general pattern of human and primate biology, and explain a number of otherwise quite unintelligible things about it. If an artist has read such interpretations he cannot forget them in writing or painting, and there is no reason why he should try.

The painter who has read and understood Freud on the releaser effects of sexual dimorphism can hardly paint the nude without thinking of them. In the past he used the same pleasure-generating or anxiety-generating devices intuitively. Now he is consciously aware of their content. Consider now the picture by the Belgian Surrealist Delvaux, which I have reproduced.[47] I think that this is an example of synthetic, or emblematic, Freudian

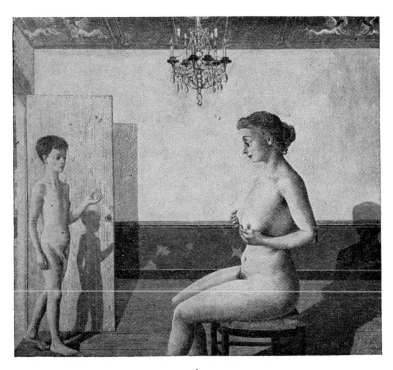

painting—that it is, in other words, a deliberate construction, not a spontaneous fantasy. I take a certain risk in saying this while the artist is alive—for it may be that he knows no more about Freud and sexual dimorphism than did Shakespeare, and that he is painting straight out of his head. The manner of treatment makes me reasonably confident, however, that he is not; I have seen three at least of his pictures which seem to be concerned explicitly with the Freudian view of the biological significance of nakedness, and if they are free fantasies rather than constructions they are, to say the least, remarkably detailed and explicit.

This one is a kind of eikon devoted to the 'exhibitionist situation' as it occurs in the Freudian view of childhood development. Delvaux appears to have painted, as fantasy, some aspects of this situation—the general sexual cathexis of nakedness, the anxiety of the child over the physical difference between the sexes, the desire to see and to be seen, the male child's advance to his mother in inviting her to admire, and reassure, his virility. Here boy and woman look at each other without alarm—floodlit, as it were, and with candles burning although it is bright daylight: she holds her breasts, to emphasise, perhaps, that she is complete in the possession of mother, while she looks at his nakedness permissively and with pleasure. It is, in fact, the psychosexual stage at which the indecent exposer is 'stuck', and that is the smile he hopes to elicit. A pre-Freudian painter would have added one further detail—he would have given the little boy wings and a bow. This is how Venus traditionally looks at Cupid in innumerable Classical, Renaissance and Baroque pieces which are equally full of symbols emphasising the sexual significance of sight—mirrors, lighted candles, emphatic eyes. The theme is fully traditional. All that has happened as a result of explanation is that the emphasis has become didactic.[48] There is another Delvaux in the Tate Gallery—in this, a fashionably-dressed woman stands looking at her naked, sleeping double, painted with photographic clarity, while background figures search for, and appear to lament, a missing object; this would do admirably for a complementary didactic piece, representing Freud's view of fashion and adornment as woman's substitute for the maleness of which she feels herself to be shorn.

I run great risk with both these pictures, but whether my guess about synthesis is right or wrong, they also admirably illustrate the way in which psychoanalysis intellectualises art, if we let it: we only see how far this intellectualisation goes when we consider a painter like Klee, whose fantasy seems as far from didacticism as any fairytale. Klee himself wrote—'Let art sound like a fairytale and be at home everywhere. . . . And to men let it be a holiday, a change of atmosphere and point of view, a transfer to another world which presents a diverting spectacle, so that they may return to everyday life with renewed vitality.'[49] Yet it would be difficult to find a more exhausting intellectual exercise than he has left the determined understander of pictures—his symbols cannot be ignored, or allowed to soak in unquestioned; the underlying structure is too provocative for us not to look for it. Art accordingly comes full circle—it begins as a device to communicate complex states without verbalising them, and ends as a provocation to verbalise in the interest of biological and psychological knowledge. What was a mystery is becoming an observation. This is a point at which we might well follow Jung's advice and 'take the dream for what it is'.

If we are soft-centred ourselves, such symbolical puzzle-reading (which cannot be meaningful, except in the most general terms, when it is done out of context, and without examining the painter's mind as well as his picture) can become a typical soft-centred game, and provoke us into constructions quite as questionable as Yeats' gyres. After looking at Delvaux one begins to notice background figures in Titian's or Lambert Sustris' pictures of the naked Venus, who are searching for something and finding—fashionable clothes. Yet if their activities are more symbolic than those of other maidservants, there is no way of proving it, and the validity of Freud's ideas about the releaser effect of sexual dimorphism, though they stand up uncommonly well to the confrontation process, need to be demonstrated by more arduous methods than choosing pictures to fit them. If he has the sense to avoid numerological enthusiasms, this gives the artist the advantage over the biologist, whether he paints out of his head or out of the book. The verbalised theory may be right or wrong—but the artist already knew intuitively, when he painted his dream picture in the older iconographic mode of Venus and Cupid, that there was *something* there, of major

71

importance, which is set in motion by that juxtaposition, and if later research were to overturn the precise Freudian interpretation, Delvaux would still have painted an agreeable picture, and one which, like its Classical predecessors, is edifying. There is still pending a correct restatement, 'something there'. 'It was not I but the poets,' said Freud, 'who discovered the Unconscious.'

The clinical value of rival psychoanalytical systems, or the synthesis between them, has to be judged from other than literary and comparative biological evidence, and is outside my competence. I am equally incompetent to comment on another point, which is theoretically very important for our ideas of art and its origins—the effect of therapeutic analysis on artists, which Kubie[50] has recently discussed. The number of artists who approach psychoanalysis—at least until more of its ideas have been tackled by fully hard-centred methods—with any informed knowledge is likely to be very small, and it will not be helped by the large amateur literature to which I am here contributing. But the effects of the analytical approach will not be delayed for accurate knowledge, and the other lines of thought which it has set in motion—in anthropology, interpretative study of folklore, and comparative religion, if not in aesthetics—are all moving in on the awareness of any artist who is not knowledge-proof. Once seen, the implications of these studies cannot be overlooked, and they make the most ignorant artist approach his material in a new light, even before a misuse of their terminology has got into the common speech. One of their consequences is to bring back didactic art, at least as inevitably as Marxism has done, and more effectively. They also, like Marxism, raise questions about the edifying and unedifying in art—a form of approach which liberal-minded people will instinctively distrust, but which we cannot logically reject out-of-hand, though the artist of conviction will act most ethically, I believe, in ignoring it. Fortunately in our society and probably in all society, true edification is on the side of revolution and humanity rather than the accepted sources of edifying matter.

The Freudian paintings I have described are edifying. They have the tranquillity which Freud attributes to a successfully completed dream-work: they discharge the function which religious ceremonies discharge more arduously and less consciously—but in them the mental operation which they carry out upon us is being directed by intelligence. They generate creative peace of mind. In another of Delvaux's pictures the same naked girl sits on her chair in the middle of the street, between the tramlines, and in the path of the approaching tram. We have no anxiety at her rashness—we know that even industrial civilisation, which stops for nothing else, must stop for her.

This communicated reassurance requires either intuition or thought from the artist—it is the reverse of neurotic art, and more purposively genuine, if anything, than its classical antecedents. Anxiety is the easiest of all spectator emotions to excite. In a culture where edifying pictures have so long been dominated by tortured saints, or at best virgin mothers, and where knowledge of the biology of mind has been exploited in art chiefly to increase its shock effect by introducing more alarming, threatening or aggressive matter, the smile of a mother-goddess whose nakedness, like that of a Hindu Surasundari, is to be desired, not feared, has a value for morale and for morality apart from any aesthetic pleasure it may give us.

IV

The Rape of Andromeda

—Ce n'est que je sois le moins inspiré du monde, mais
j'ai envie de voir ça—c'est une sorte de curiosité et comme
qui dirait un désir lubrique sans érection . . .

GUSTAVE FLAUBERT (of *Salammbô*)

NOT long ago the respective critics of the *New Statesman* and
the *Spectator* described an adventure story[51] by Mr. Ian
Fleming as 'without doubt the nastiest book I have ever
read'[52] and as 'providing sheer entertainment such as I, who must
read many novels, am seldom lucky enough to find.'[53] Comment
has been made on the popularity of this writer with Cabinet
Ministers. Some years ago George Orwell wrote of the very
different novels of Mr. Mickey Spillane and Mr. James Hadley
Chase (who were supposed to have a similar social range of
popularity in America) that 'Freud and Macchiavelli have
reached the outer suburbs'.

Mr. Spillane and Mr. Chase specialise in affectless violence. Mr.
Fleming is more gentlemanly (it was his upper-class hero who
provoked the *New Statesman*) and specialises in masochistic
fantasy in erotic settings—he has given Bulldog Drummond a
sex life. All three have attracted hostile notice directed at a *genre*;
I would describe the *genre* itself as the erotic comic-book for
literate adults. The pictorial comic-book reflects so well the
psychodynamic state of its parent society (which it is often
accused of producing) that it is not surprising to find non-
pictorial comic-books written for the literate, or read—if the
remarks about Cabinet Ministers are correct—by those who are

74

themselves engaged in writing the comic-book fantasy of contemporary history: 'Monk' Lewis was a member of Parliament. Such books belong to erotic literature, but the erotic literature of a culture which operates a selective censorship against normality—they therefore deal, as a rule, not with love but with hate, the cult of sexual and general violence, and the ghoulish. This cult is distasteful, though the violence of the attack on it in some quarters has itself the appearance of excitement at the matter attacked: it is also traditional. Mario Praz'[54] catalogue of the morbid preoccupations of the Romantics—sadism, diabolism, the character of woman as Medusa and bitch, the exaltation of suffering and corruption—is a statement of the emotional handicaps which have affected Western art intermittently since the second century, not the nineteenth. The only new feature of Baudelaire's 'petrarchising over the disgusting' is the lack of the devotional tone which would bring it into line with St. Augustine. When there is a critical row about these tendencies, it is still directed at those authors who dilute them with references to normal sexuality. They are now the predominant matter of commercial entertainment: in the comic-book they are reduced to pictorial psychosymbols without the literary cover they have previously had—in the literary-comic the psychosymbols go back into literary form, still indecently exposed. The essence of this form is that its effect depends on *motif*, not manner, and that the plot is a pretext for the incident: this is equally true of more pretentious literature, but in the case of the literary-comic the fact is frankly recognised by all; the novelist's first need is a good knowledge or intuition for the natural history of human sexual response to situational symbols. Now and then he can be too good—part of the adverse comment on the three writers I mentioned, especially Mr. Fleming, is due to their ability to free-associate (or read up and put in) really threatening psychoanalytical matter in a bare form. Part is due to uneasiness among liberal readers to see such matter made unpleasantly real at a time when history and psychotic fantasy are dangerously convergent. For them, the comic-book threatens both social morals and polite fiction—which already contains the same material, but better-wrapped.

Gothic *Schauer-romantik* is by now a popular dissertation

75

subject. The interesting thing about the literary 'comic-book' is that it owes little to Gothicism—less than the modern serious or 'unpopular' novel. The writers of the literary-comic are going further back, if not for their inspiration, at least for their precedent, for the novel did not generate the literary-comic: phylogenetically, the literary-comic generated the novel, in the society of second- and third-century Alexandria, which also generated our literary morals. Alexandrian novels include the most likeable of all erotic stories, *Daphnis and Chloe,* but the manner of Longus assorted ill with the growth of Christendom: the modern literary-comic mimics in incident, though not in spirit of style, other romances of the same period which are far more familiar in key. I am not so sure about Mr. Spillane, but Mr. Fleming has his ancestry there—possibly in Achilles Tatius, whose *Cleitophon and Leucippe* is the best and most characteristic of literary-comics, with something of the modern pace, and almost all of the modern psychosymbolic obsessions.

Modern alarm over them, among reviewers, calls for an experiment. The comic-book qualities of Tatius are real. I will exaggerate them unfairly for demonstration purposes by cataloguing the incidents of this romance out of their rather ornate context, as if I were the *New Statesman's* psychosymbolist reviewer. It begins relatively quietly: in the first two books, hero meets heroine, and saves her from a rival who has hired pirates to abduct her, by arranging for his own unwanted fiancée to be abducted in her place. An assignation follows, but Leucippe's virginity is saved by an ill-omened dream which wakes her mother (there is a suggestion that what happens later is a judgment on her for trying to dispose of it). The lovers talk their way out of this situation, and run away together. The events which follow are much more familiar in content. They are shipwrecked (Book III), captured by bandits, bound hand and foot and deposited in a hut. Cleitophon is rescued by the Egyptian army, but the bandits have removed Leucippe as a human sacrifice, and he is obliged to watch while she is staked out, disembowelled and partially eaten. She has somehow survived this procedure, and jumps out of her coffin, bloodstained and still eviscerate, to embrace him—the whole performance turns out to have been a mummery, conducted with a bladder full of guts and a collapsible dagger (one of Mr. Fleming's heroines, who is exposed, in a similar posture, to be eaten by crabs, escapes with the same inconsequential aplomb—the crabs, she explains, were vegetarians). The reunion is short-lived, for in Book IV Leucippe suddenly goes mad—Cleitophon is obliged to tie her up once more, this time for her own good, while he traces the source of the miscarried love-philtre which is responsible, beats up a suitable informant, and obtains the antidote; Leucippe recovers (Book V) in time to be carried off by more pirates, hired this time by the beaten informant; when Cleitophon seems likely to overtake them, they cut off her head and throw the body overboard. Cleitophon, *faute de mieux*, kisses her severed neck farewell, buries her with a literary oration in the worst and most ornate Alexandrian taste, and goes glumly home, where he learns—as his readers could have told him—that they need never have eloped at all.

He now forms a liaison with the passionate widow Melitta, and sails for her estate, refusing meanwhile to sleep with her out of deference to Leucippe's memory (a ploy for endless politer fiction, this). On arrival he is accosted by a fettered and crop-headed slave-girl who tells him a story of beatings and ill-usage: she is, of course, Leucippe herself, deprived of her hair, like Hemingway's Maria, but still a virgin. She is recognised by her handwriting, not her person—with her physical configuration Cleitophon is, for a lover, remarkably unfamiliar; he has been fobbed off once already with a substitute corpse. At this point Melitta's deceased husband appears, beats up Cleitophon, and puts *him* in fetters. Melitta releases him from these in exchange for a reluctant but very satisfactory embrace (poor Melitta! She is a real person lost in this gallimaufry): he is imprisoned on a charge of adultery, told that Leucippe is dead, beaten up twice, tied up once more, this time as a prelude to torture, but saved by a religious amnesty—and the lovers are united after a trial of virginity in which Leucippe, like her great-great-granddaughter Miss Blandish, proves providentially undamaged.

Although this is a preposterous plot, my selective outline is grossly unfair to an entertaining novel—what I have done is to treat it as reviewers have treated Mr. Spillane and Mr. Fleming, or as Dr. Praz has treated the Romantics, and this does no justice to its literary importance. This particular romance generated not only *Candide* but, by way of Sidney's *Arcadia*, a sizeable part of the modern European novel; the genealogy is neatly marked by the fact that in borrowing the sham decapitation Sidney named his heroine Pamela. It may be typical episcopal reading, but I have cheated by pitching the summary in Mr. Fleming's key. The effect of the original is neither Hollywood nor, as it could easily be, Evelyn Waugh; the whole performance is by modern standards quite un-nasty even when it is sophisticated, and never satirical, though now and then it is quietly ironic. The author is a rhetorician: his hokum is diluted with polite and erudite chatter on subjects from natural history to mythology and painting, a little in the manner of the *Swiss Family Robinson*; except for Melitta, who deserves better companions, there is no characterisation to alarm, and after one resurrection we feel no more anxiety for Leucippe than for the woman whom the conjurer saws in half. Some episodes recall the disturbing but fabulous matter of the nursery tales, in which decapitated and revived princesses have their ancestry—others have echoes of the *Magic Flute* and the sham ordeals of Masonic initiation: the sufferings of the lovers are a game, evoking no more protest than a children's game of captives and executions where the heroine will be called in from the stake to tea.

Yet compared with other romances, compared with Apuleius or Heliodorus, or even Xenophon of Ephesus—whose hero is crucified, falls into the Nile cross and all, and sails down the river on it, while his heroine is being put in a pit full of wild dogs—Tatius is tangibly nearer the comic-book tradition. The comic-book is a story which is a pretext for sexually-coloured psycho-symbolic incidents where the theme, not the treatment, is the selling point. In the picture version there is no literary development—all *Vorlust* and no *Endlust*, in the modern literary version the linking matter is perfunctory, depending on the trouble the author cares to take with it: in Tatius the literary matter is ornate but quite irrelevant. In all three, the alarming incidents are affectless or the affect is inappropriate. And Tatius, in contrast to the even longer-winded Heliodorus, has something more like the modern speed.

Tatius is also closer to the comic-book than Longus or Apuleius in what he leaves out. This is supposed to be a love-story, but unlike *Daphnis and Chloe,* or the *Golden Ass* and the *Satiricon,* which are not love stories at all in principle, it is strikingly asexual. Cleitophon's ostentatious refusal of his legitimate opportunity with Melitta might be taken as knightly fidelity, but suggests more than that; there are lyrical accounts of the preliminaries, accessories and frustrations of love, but the enthusiasm of fulfilment is dissipated on the captivities and repeated deaths, and the lovers' final union is celebrated when it comes in the single sentence 'We arrived at Byzantium, where we celebrated the marriage for which we had so long prayed, and thence set out for Tyre.'

Alexandrine rhetoricians were not given to under-writing or to divine reticence. The Hays Code is at work. It is not Tatius' code —when Cleitophon gratifies Melitta adulterously to get out of prison, after refusing to enjoy her legitimately as a widow, he puts in a passage to the effect that love needs no cushions, which reads like an ironic manifesto. The throw-away of the wedding night itself looks like irony at someone's expense. His lovers are only chaste, in the first place at least, because they are interrupted. This is 'erotic' literature in a different tradition from that in which Daphnis and Chloe on their wedding night slept no more than two birds of the night. Xenophon's Habrocome and Anthea, whose adventures are just as hair-raising, are married in the first book. And even Eustatius' much later Byzantine lovers—two of the nicest in literature, before they have to leave on the conventional assault course—do a good deal of providentially-interrupted petting.[55] Tatius foreshadows the literature of conventional chivalry, but he also foreshadows the modern and premodern literature of impotence. This has been called a 'panegyric of chastity',[56] and one is aware off-stage of a virulent contemporary monasticism which regarded woman as evil and suffering as an acceptable substitute; in which martyrdom as a prelude to resurrection was the only decent form of sexual excitement, and in which Origen castrated himself physically as well as emotionally. Tatius rather than Longus sets the key of the literary-erotic tradition of Christendom: it is with suffering, not women, that his readers are already expected to be in love.

The rest of this genealogy is well worth following for its own sake. The most striking note in Tatius' romance, in view of its literary progeny, is the stock rhetorician's device by which it is held together—each section begins with the description of a picture seen by chance in a temple or an art shop, a *chose vue* which sets the key to the impending incident. The first of these pictures, which appear like Tarot cards to predict the fortunes of the story, is of Europa and the bull, and it prefaces two books of more or less realistic domestic incident; these include the abduction of the unwanted fiancée by pirates, engineered in part by the hero, and his own elopement with Leucippe. The third book begins with the description of two more pictures, which forecast darker events and an impending change of mood; one of Andromeda, the other of Prometheus, the distressed heroine and the distressed hero, accompanied by an ill-omened dream. Tatius goes out of his way to rub in the significance of these figures; both are bound, both are unjustly tormented, both are on the point of rescue. The bondage *motif*, the torture of Prometheus and his release, are to be reflected in the details of the episode of disembowelling and revival. Book V, and the second sham death, is preceded by another symbol of ill-omen—this time the tapestry woven by Philomela to show her rape by Tereus, and her revenge in making him eat his son. But fortunately we know that the actors in this sinister legend, turned to birds, remember their sufferings only in their songs—so, in the final chapters (if the novel is indeed complete) the story and its lovers make a perfect landing where they began, in ordinary life and at a different level of existence—they wake up, as it were, to normality.

This device of the pictures is used with rather startling psychoanalytical insight. Tatius might have been reading Róheim, and in his choice of Andromeda and Prometheus to preside over the story, he has accurately selected the tutelary deities of European Romanticism, and of the emotional disabilities which have perpetually haunted it.

This is not the first appearance of Andromeda in Alexandrian novels. The plot of Heliodorus' *Aethiopica* turns on a changeling heroine, an Ethiopian princess born white instead of black because at the moment of her conception her mother had looked too hard at the white body of her ancestress Andromeda in a family portrait. By the same prenatal influence she is destined to be abducted, tormented, chained and unsuccessfully burned at the stake for ten books, before being united to her lover, who has meanwhile undergone similar hardships, wrestled with bulls, and narrowly escaped death as a human sacrifice: through her mother's lack of concentration she has fallen under the dominion of the Goddess of Comic-books. For Andromeda is not only the captive princess of chivalry who is there to be rescued—she is the Misfortunes of Virtue; she symbolises the ambivalence of literature towards tormented maidens; according to the Roman astrologers those born under her constellation are neither heroes, nor even damsels in distress, but professional torturers—

> supplicium vectigal erit. . qui denique posset
> pendentem e scopulis ipsam spectare puellam
> vinctorum dominus. sociusque in parte catenae[57]

and Perseus carries in his hand the Gorgon's head, the anatomical and moral *équivoque* of Womanhood, the sight of which, like the evil eye, can turn to stone. Tatius makes Prometheus Andromeda's male twin. They are unjustly condemned, male and female. In their constructive moments they have been pity and liberty, chivalry and revolution: but they have a number of darker avatars as the gratuitously ill-used heroine, and the victim of the tormentor-father—the revolutionary and erotic images which alternate so disconcertingly in *The Revolt of Islam*.

Andromeda and Prometheus are unacquainted figures from unrelated myths; the Alexandrian novel fuses the suffering hero and the suffering heroine into a combination new to literature, which is to dominate it from then on, the lovers who suffer together instead of sleeping together—for whom, in later writers, death will be the eventual orgasm, *la mort doulce* translated from the ecstasies of coition to those of simultaneous death. With a few exceptions (Hero and Leander—Haemon and Antigone) this is not a theme of Classical literature, where lovers die of grief, or for revenge—but it is a theme of Christian martyrology, and it was destined to become perhaps the most popular single *motif* in European literature: sometimes merely decorative, as the tortured saints of the holy pictures are decorative, sometimes with the whole Romantic empathy behind it. When Shelley came to use it he by-passed the literary tradition in which dying lovers were a conventional source of tragic endings, and took his material at one remove from its Alexandrine origin, and with its original erotic significance intact; his martyred lovers are lifted from Tasso, as Tasso had borrowed from Heliodorus. Shelley adjusted the story to suit his own psychological requirements: Tasso's Olindo joins his unrequiting beloved at the stake after an unsuccessful attempt to save her by a false confession, and laments, in words very like those of Cleitophon to Leucippe, that these are not the bonds he hoped to see unite them; Shelley's Cythna volunteers to die with Laon, simply, it appears, to complete their mutual ecstasy: Olindo and Sophronia are rescued—Laon and Cythna wake, after a spectacular combustion, in the post-orgasmal repose of a Shelleyan paradise. On their way through the Renaissance the symbols of love and torment have now acquired a cathexis and an intensity quite foreign to Tatius or Heliodorus, but familiar enough to the modern reader.

In Shelley, the gallery of unfortunate virtue is complete—Prometheus punished by Zeus, Beatrice Cenci exposed as victim not of a decently reticent monster, but to the incestuous assaults of a father who talks very like de Sade; and finally the lovers of *The Revolt of Islam,* translated from the stake to a Baroque landscape in a fantasy of really alarming intensity, where sexual excitement, masochism, lyrical poetry and revolutionary politics are inextricable and interchangeable. This mixture was evidently not to everybody's taste: Shelley defended the work against the protests of his friends with the same well-justified candour as Flaubert—'The poem was produced by a series of thoughts which filled my mind with sustained and unbounded enthusiasm. . . . I felt that it was in many respects a genuine picture of my own mind.' The same psychosymbolic material is exploited in *The Cenci,* and finally tamed in *Prometheus,* but it is in the extended form of *The Revolt of Islam* that the self-identification is most wholehearted. There is certainly no better example of a work, or a series of works, in which a compulsive fantasy has produced great literature. By the end of the century, the *motif* of shared bondage and death as a decent and more ecstatic form of coition has become completely explicit—in *Hassan,* or *Les Noyades*—and is even present in a muffled form in improbable works like *The Last of the Mohicans.*

The Rape of Andromeda

Pegasus, the symbol of imaginative literature, sprang from the blood of the Gorgon. In psychoanalytical terms this seems to be abundantly true, at least of our own literature, but Freud might also have pointed out that it is this particular Gorgon which petrified the emotional development of an entire culture, to make Andromeda's chains more desirable than her person.

So much for the remoter ancestry of the literary 'comic'—what of its present and future? If Freudian concepts account for the content of literary forms, the reasons for their prevalence at a given time seem to be chiefly social.

The sub-sexual pulp novel, with or without an exotic cast, and still more its middle-class equivalents, seem to represent a thoroughgoing return of the European novel to one of its origins, and may well represent its future. All the characteristic features—the arbitrary plot linking a series of sexually-coloured but technically chaste episodes, the displacement of physical sexuality by torments and misfortunes, and the typical irrelevance of the linking commentary, which are features of this commercial *genre* today—were present in the works which set the key of the European novel. The Hays Code and its literary progeny were born together. There is no hokum in Hollywood which these early novels do not anticipate, and strikingly little difference in the formula they had to fill, apart from an added requirement of stylistic elaboration.

Hokum is the stock-in-trade of the story teller. It never fails, even with those too highbrow to admit its appeal, and if it appears in Alexandrine rhetoricians it does so as freely in the *Arabian Nights* and in Shakespeare. When literary forms lose interest as literature, there is always hokum to fall back on, and it has played a quite remarkable part in providing inspiration for serious writers. The similarity between the late Alexandrine novel and the matter of pulp fiction and television—as well as the cause of its germinal influence on European fiction generally—is in the selection of permissible fantasies. Heliodorus, speed apart, might have written the script for any of the more restrained Hollywood exotics—unlike Longus, who makes sexuality natural and charming, or Apuleius, who enjoyed it and satirised it, the

83

novelists who exerted most influence on the subsequent development of fiction were, as we have seen, precisely those who
obeyed something similar to the Hays Code in their selection of
permissible fantasy, and the consequences are similar.

Moral censorship has given our Anglo-American culture an
erotic art which is uniquely odd, being commercially produced
out of an expert knowledge of the natural history of prudery and
of the commoner audience-drawing fetishes. Indeed, the natural
history of response to hokum, especially sexual hokum, in our
society is even more interesting than its psychodynamics. The
cathexis attached to suffering, and especially masochism, seems to
be more intense in the audience of 'serious' than of popular literature. (A side effect of this is that the tragic dénouement has now a
strong prestige significance—it is evidence of 'serious' intention,
even if it has to be dragged in as arbitrarily as the last-minute
rescues of romance.) The 'serious' work must end on a note of
frustration—'happy' endings are stigmatic of a lower form of
literature. The algolagnia of popular literature is by contrast of
a robust kind. It prefers fights, beatings, bindings and danger-
situations which are physical and have to that extent a genital
reference: it avoids the much less healthy refinements of purely
mental suffering; and masochism is popular only if it does not go
too far. Popular self-identification will stand up to a threat of
combustion or drowning in aphrodisiac circumstances, and find
it agreeable, but it knows where to stop—ecstasies pushed to the
point of decease, like those of Laon or *Les Noyades,* have no
future in them. Women, perhaps for physiological reasons, seem
willing to venture further: they will accompany the heroine up
to and including her actual demise—'What a loverly death to
die!', as Nellie Wallace used to sing—but there must be at least
a celestial choir between them and the darkness of annihilation.

These sex differences in response and readership have an
important effect on popular erotic iconography. Kinsey points
out that women do not respond erotically to printed matter
anything like as predictably as men, and consequently do not
read it for direct physical stimulation—there is a whole literature
addressed to them in which the erotic component is social. Many
of the excesses of the 'tough' commercial romance are due to the
fact that it is addressed only to men: the heroines are expendable,

and not for self-identification, while the two-seater fantasy of Tatius and of the cinema, by contrast, is to some extent moderated by the fact that it must suit readers of both sexes. Others are sacrificed, quite arbitrarily, to an extension of the Hays convention over adultery: the wages of sexuality are death. Even Hemingway's Catherine goes this way. Hemingway justifies this on the ground that there can be no happy ending to a true marriage. But the disseverer of pleasant societies intervenes needlessly soon.

We seem in one sense, so far as popular fiction is concerned, to be going back, in the inverse sense of the sequence which produced the dying lovers of Tatius and Shelley. They are losing popularity: we are almost back with Andromeda who is characterless—and, in place of Perseus or Prometheus, the gangster-policeman-special agent born under her constellation. Sometimes he will love her, sometimes he will kill her—not infrequently he will do both, and to a succession of women. We are also back (far more significantly) with a limited amount of genital sexuality among all the killings. The *genre* has been called 'sex and violence' fiction. It is arranged pyramidally: soft-backed novels on newsprint at the bottom, glossy paper-covers for the middle classes, hard backs for Cabinet Ministers and the established, and even literature at the top.

At the bottom of the pyramid, rape now supplements murder —near the top, Bulldog Drummond has gone into partnership with Lautréamont and developed an explicit sex-life. With the second of these events I for one would not quarrel. The objectionableness of the modern version lies not in the erotic significance it gives to violence, and least of all in the return of some normal love-making, but in its quality of affectlessness in brutality. This is alarming because we have seen it recently in real life. However, not all sadistic imagery is cruel, and not all cruelty is sadistic: a good deal of the violence in modern literature is spiteful rather than erotic. The authors of paper-backs do not need to manufacture machinery to revive their corpses—the corpses are perfectly acceptable dead. These corpses, moreover, are not Elizabethan, or even Gothic—they are mechanically and affectlessly produced; they purge no emotions because they excite none. They are simply required as décor to produce potency. In older erotic romances, the plot, however arbitrary, is a means of preserving the decencies, and showing that the game, even if it is bloodthirsty, *is* still a game. The modern romance has no use for nursery games. Accordingly the better it is done, the more alarming it becomes. It may be that there is greater sincerity in accepting the fact that if, in real life, you shoot your woman she will die without benefit of coincidence: modern readers would probably be insulted by mummery with fake bullet-holes, though I think Mr. Fleming, who is nearest of his contemporaries to the spirit of Tatius, would consider them if he had to. The realistic and social aspect of the 'sex and violence' hero is his least likeable: Tatius and even de Sade do not threaten our everyday self-control, whereas Mr. Mickey Spillane does.

Critical anger over such matter still depends on the content of sex, not the proportion of violence. 'Sex and violence' is in all respects an improvement, in my view, on violence alone, even if sex has entered the firm only as a junior partner. Much of literary history since the time of Tatius has been taken up with the attempts of the public to get, and writers to give them, an erotic literature dealing with adult sexual behaviour, and the efforts of a disturbed minority to keep normality out in favour of decent sadism and masochism—to which, so long as they have no genital references, there is no moral objection. If Mr. Spillane had written a contemporary *Daphnis and Chloe* it would have been banned: *Chastelard* was indignantly attacked by our grandfathers, not for the hero's erotic rhapsody over decapitation, but because he hid under Queen Mary's bed, and the art of the pornographer, if one can call it that, has long consisted in trying to introduce among decent, patriotic and even devout abnormality the elements of normal sex which will make it sell.

Sadistic fantasy in a frankly sexual context is itself less mischievous, since less likely to erupt in overt behaviour, than rationalised sadistic fantasies outside one, and much less infectious by example. There are not many people who imitate Jack the Ripper, and those who do so can be segregated; but there are a great many Conservative Party Congress delegates who yell their support for flogging, and they can neither be segregated nor shamed.

We can see another and more specifically sexual origin for

pulp-novel violence in the stereotype of the heroines—or the lay figures—with whom the routine of sex-and-violence is enacted. At least they are responsive. They rub themselves against the impending ravisher like cats, they throb, bite, scratch and emit ecstatic cries—they are the women of the Sanskrit erotic textbooks, which we shall encounter later, and which classify with great thoroughness several dozen varieties of love-bites, excitatory scratch-marks, erotic blows, and exclamations in intercourse. These women behave, in short, as women of some cultures appear to have behaved, as the reader's girl friend or wife does not, and as he very probably wishes she would.

Geoffrey Gorer remarks of sex-and-violence literature that 'despite all the prohibitions of convention and law people do acquire sexual experience, and for the greater part find out that they have been stuffed with lies—that though pleasant it is not such lasting ecstasy and final solution as art would leave us to suppose; and then they are ready for the other half of our myth, violence'.[58]

When anyone finds that orchestral music, though pleasant, is overrated, I am inclined to suspect either a lack of musical sensibility or the effects of an inferior performance. The public estimate is not all derived from fable—it represents also a shrewd intuition that the performance they are attending is not of concert standard. It is very largely the failure of our society to develop its erotic life in the proper context which makes it such a prey to the desire for 'kicks' of all kinds. One has to be extraordinarily lucky, in our society, to meet one nymphomaniac in a lifetime. The ravisher or the lover of the pulp novel (they are synonymous) pummels and manhandles his victim although she is responsive. His reader has perhaps to restrain himself from pummelling the woman who lies so disappointingly still, in order to obtain some reaction, any reaction, in response. And what in a less sexually-anxious society is a game, to be played hard, but not rough, and certainly not foul, is in our society interpreted as a child is apt to interpret a glimpse of adult coition—as an alarming piece of violence, carrying with it the stigma which, in a humane society, is attached to violence in general. People in our society do not often observe each other's sexual performance, or even, being otherwise occupied, their own. The *con brio* description by

d'Annunzio in *Forse che si* is in its essentials only an accurate
piece of field natural history, the normal coital responses of a
rather demonstrative couple; it is the author who misinterprets
their superficially alarming and paroxysmal behaviour as a
Martian would misinterpret the facial expression of a winning
miler. Some of the violence of the purely sexual component in
pulp fiction comes from the same source, less accurately observed
for lack of the opportunity of observation. Copyright presents
difficulties of quotation: I hope that this already-quoted example
is genuine, for it is certainly typical—

> 'I started to open her dress fiercely, but I was all thumbs with
> excitement. She showed me how, in between a mixture of whimpers
> and passionate gasps. And then ... we met like a pair of savage
> animals ...'

Mink, perhaps, or the Jack Dempsey fish (*Cichlisoma*) which
prefaces its pairing—less spectacular than ours—with a really
spectacular fight, which is anything but symbolic. If the heroines
of this literature do nothing else, they ensure selection for the
vigour of their progeny:

> 'She didn't budge as I leaned over and tore off her dress in one. Then
> her negligée—that split like a burst sheath. I guess she thought
> passive resistance would beat me, so she went all stiff.
>
> 'But now it was my turn to see plenty—and this time her eyes had
> a kinda excited fear in them. But she still wasn't for moving, and
> that made things sorta difficult at first. So I whipped my belt off and
> strapped her arms to the bedhead. Then I kissed her, hard; she bit
> back at me till the blood spurted from my lips.
>
> 'By this time I sure was wild. And she—she was moaning and
> frantic with passion. "Cut me free—tear me" she moaned. I tore her
> alright—all strapped up, just like that.'[59]

This is hardly sadism, except in its technical sense: it is merely
enthusiastic coition seen through the keyhole by an inexperienced
adolescent and embroidered—a violent, convulsive and noisy
business, which makes him wonder if this particular Andromeda
is being rescued or murdered, and whether he ought not to
interfere. The embroidery is notably inexperienced—Durtal in
Là-Bas artfully removed his braces before the arrival of a
potential mistress, to avoid undignified interruptions; the idea

of tearing a woman's clothes off her back indicates only a lack of field trial—(there is the same lack of practicality in most of the hand-to-hand fights which fill the intervals between rapes in these books, the writers, like Melanie Klein's babies, vastly overrating their physical powers of causing injury).

It looks as if the hard-back and soft-back reader have one anxiety in common, whether they ravish women or only bite them: the object in each case is to secure response; unnecessary, one would have thought, with such provocative women, unless it is only a game.

In cultures which do not confuse violence in love with brutality elsewhere, it could indeed be no more than a game, played fully in accordance with the rules. The protagonists bite one another according to the principles of *dasanacchedya*: even Andromeda's chains are *mekhalābandha*—the tying-up routine undergone by every comic-book heroine and most comic-book heroes from Tatius to Sapper, which in our culture is a common compulsive ritual, and a mainstay of the trade in decent erotic photographs, is elsewhere a conventional amatory technique with no obvious anxiety behind it: Moroccan bridegrooms, according to Westermark, even delegate it to the best man.[60] As for the concomitant erotic frenzy—

> the horse with the bit between his teeth sees neither the sticks nor the water, and two lovers in the struggle of pleasure take no heed for blows, knocks or death itself. But the man should consider the girl's pleasure in this, and behave accordingly.
>
> (Kokkoka, *Ratirahasya*)

What is depressing, therefore, about Hoggart's lovers is not their boisterousness but their anxiety and their unadult lack of all finer feelings, in love or elsewhere. Whereas in real life these lovers would recover their breath, a little bruised and embarrassed by their own vehemence, the characters of fiction keep up the same pre-orgasmal frenzy in their other activities.

These activities are brutal, and either criminal or justified because the persons assaulted are criminals; the sexual violence, too, is generally not passionate but merely nasty, and in earnest. This consequence flows directly from the other sources of the popularity of the *genre* at all levels of society. Society conscripts the unestablished reader and kicks him around—if we were not too well brought up we would kick society back: established or unestablished respectability has an ill-defined association with the disappointing frigidity of our women: rough stuff, in our folk-lore, at least makes women respond, if only by protest. Therefore let us imagine ourselves gangsters, able to kick society, occupationally brutal, whose women are disreputably responsive—if not the misfortunes of virtue, at least the prosperities of vice. Better if we have something substantial to lose from gangsterism, let us be a law above the law—we can then beat the gangsters (who deserve it) and enjoy their women, with a genuflection to righteousness—we have a civilised dislike of violent criminals in real life, and in any case we do not want to be sent down as delinquents.

Hoggart does not give the source of his example—it appears to come from 'unestablished' popular fiction, without glossy covers, and though representative, it is already a little behind the times. Erotic sub-fiction is getting steadily more sophisticated, and, at the same time, coming to reflect middle-class tastes in fantasy—masochism instead of sadism, and modern plumbing. The heroines of paper novels in the 1900s were seduced by their creators' idea of a rich waster in their audience's idea of a Mayfair flat. The new conventions are increasingly those of readers with some experience of love-making in conditions of privacy and with running hot water. At the top of the pyramid the backs are no longer paper, and the experience of the fictional heroes greater. Mr. Fleming's 'James Bond', the most experienced of these heroes, and an ex-Naval Commander, does not—I think I am right in saying—commit rape, nor imagine he can conveniently undress a woman by brute force. He confines himself to willing subjects and has the sense to ask first if they are virgins, though he may bite them as a purely erotic stimulus. The rest of his time is occupied, not so much in killing people, as in being tortured. It is the tone of officerly experience which does the damage here, for it extends to all the masochistic routines which the eponymous hero undergoes, often in confined spaces which suggest either a Rankian birth-trauma, or, more probably, memories of engine-room duty. That it is masochism rather than sadism is itself an indication of a *genre* rising in the world and covering-up a little; recently the fantasy is schizoid rather than doggedly mechanical.

The soft-back reader, by contrast, still has a realistic perception that in matters of fact it is more blessed to give than to receive, whatever happens in fantasy. It takes the hard-back reader to save face by making at least a token appearance at the receiving end. In one sense this is reminiscent of Alexandria. Cleitophon was a suffering hero; he seldom effectively resists assault, though once a particularly violent assailant cuts a hand on his front teeth— and the capture of his girl, or even her impending murder, is more likely to stimulate rhetoric than really efficient interference. Unlike Heliodorus' Theagenes he gives no displays of super-human daring, and the only woman who solicits him as James Bond is solicited ('I want it all, James, everything you've ever done to a girl. Now. Quickly!'[61]) does not get it, at least not until later. But then Cleitophon has no firearms. And he is not an officer.

I cannot help feeling that the masochism of the Establishment is not so much decency as cover. It has the ominous half-in-earnest air which 'interrogated' persons describe in real-life tormentors. Mr. Fleming's hero chivalrously plays the victim, but I would not trust him to question any Cypriots, of either sex. The Alexandrine hero was spineless, perhaps, but decent and unofficial. The Elizabethan villain—Aaron or Vargas—was painfully moral in his Crowleyan protestations of deliberate wickedness. He does not stand for the approved conduct of society, nor represent the product of a bad public school. But the 'special agent'—who tortures suspects, ravishes women and for preference shoots them afterwards, is the emissary of society—or at least he stands for authority and its uses, for the unlimited rights of aggressive behaviour which it confers, and he is expected to carry the admiring acquiescence of his readers. The modern 'erotic' hero at the Establishment level is a professional, official, and, in Britain, upper-class bully with enough masochism in him to make him obedient and a little less aware of other people's feelings. When he is cynical, as in Mr. Spillane, one can take him as satire; he is at his least lovable when he is attached to illiterate, contemporary political stereotypes—Bulldog Drummond's 'paci-fists' or Mr. Fleming's 'Russians' and 'chingroes' (half-Chinese, half-Negro), in a schizophrenic background. Unfortunately he is also at his most realistic; history is anticipating fantasy. If

Richard Hannay was a secret agent and a gentleman (in spite of his squalid xenophobia and anti-Semitism) his duties did not in those days include conducting 'interrogations' on the Algerian pattern, and taking turns at undergoing them, or inflicting them on colleagues, by way of training. The world demand for such heroes seems to be increasing steadily, as henchmen for chaster and better-rationalised delinquents. Literature will probably not create them, but it could conceivably educate them. No well-read adolescent, even if he had never been trained to fight 'terrorists', would now need to go back to Damhouder's 'Praxis Rerum Criminalium' to find out how to torture somebody. The attitude of such hero-villains to women is of a piece with the rest of their activities. The Greek Perseus left Andromeda on her rock while he haggled with her parents—Mr. Fleming's hero would certainly rescue her, but might make love to her *in situ*: Mr. Spillane's hero, who 'specialises in shooting women in the belly', would presumably rape her first and give her to the monster afterwards.

Much has been made of the class background of this official hero. I doubt if he has any political planning behind him—nobody, that is, as Mr. Legman points out,[62] has sat down like Pharaoh and said 'Come, and let us deal wisely with them'. He has appeared like all literary figures in response to the general climate of the times, even if that includes the class anxieties which George Orwell saw in him. But he meets a need of government (all government) which a genuinely erotic literature—one, that is, concerned primarily with the physical expression of love rather than hate—cannot meet. The selectivity of censorship towards sex and in favour of violence has for the most part unconscious origins—but, at the same time, it is no accident that the sort of people who demand an asexual literature are often also the sort of people who control governments and are willing to condone thuggery by proxy—the springs of prudery, of brutality and of ambition are very often the same. And even if leaderships are not drawn, like volunteer censorships, from emotionally-handicapped people, obedient violence will in any case be more popular with administrations than love. They need manly (and unscrupulous) men; it is not easy to fit the individual who 'hugs his kicksy-wicksy here at home, that should sustain the bound and high curvet of Mars his fiery steed' into the machine of comic-book politics. He is lacking in proper offensive spirit—mushy, in fact. Men who get more pleasure from beating up Cypriots, Algerians or Hungarians than from staying at home with the girls are an administrative godsend—men in love, by contrast, tend to be at once tiresomely unwarlike in the cause of Civilisation and violently combative in resisting civic privileges such as conscription or deportation. In fact, when a man does hit back at the machine, love, not principle, is usually behind it.

To this extent the change from last century's recipe of violence alone, the prescribed material for generating manly youths with no sentimental nonsense about them, seems to represent an advance in erotic fiction if only a small one. If the authors of literary-comics are working off abnormal preoccupations, I doubt if their readers are—to anything like the same extent. There are several possible reasons other than formal sadism for the popularity of literary violence with the audience—conscripts, young industrial workers, clerks—who are the chief readers of paper-backed novels. (I am less satisfied about the readers of hard-backed novels.) One is the exasperation of current affairs, of life in a society which is two-faced, run by advertisers and confidence men who talk glibly about terminating human history if necessary, and who are equipped with powers of conscription— a society none the less in which, through the advent of order and of humane ideas, there are no accessible heads to punch. The bears, dogs and cocks which our ancestors maltreated are protected today against transferred aggression as effectively as Prime Ministers, and much more justly. Zeus has a police escort—even the vulture has the Wild Birds Protection Act behind it.

This is the result of a real and important gain in humane sensibility and in civilised behaviour. The ages of faith discharged their irrational aggressions in austerity and persecution; the eighteenth century, to judge from its sports and punishments, in public brutality. We have largely renounced these activities— the super-irrationalities of nuclear weapons and the Cold War do not replace them, because these are primarily the fabrication of a very small minority of persons in office, foisted by them on publics which are at least uneasy and at most quiescent. There is no private outlet for irrational aggression compatible with our self-respect. The proper alternative is to transmute it into rational direct action—purposive and if possible level-headed resentment against abuses, and if necessary against persons, which will bring the rest of society into line with its own moral pretensions. But this is much too hard a discipline for most intellectuals, and the eighteen-year-old conscript, facing the entire apparatus of stage-management, beset by the traps set for him by political leaders, and unused to concerted action without orders, finds this task of transmuting mere resentment into effective action intellectually difficult, personally dangerous, and often beyond him altogether. Could one help him? One could certainly try. Commercial popular art studies the natural history of its audience very carefully. More dedicated writers might learn from doing the same.

Max Nordau[63] predicted, in an unamiable frame of mind, that humanity would eventually cease to produce art altogether, and took as an example the way in which dancing, which is the most important and significant cultural activity in primitive societies, has steadily lost significance until it has become an amusement.

I think this view greatly misconceives the nature of art, but what Nordau says here of art in general is certainly true of individual art forms, and I think it might well be true of the novel. We now produce two kinds of literature, popular and unpopular. While in our public mind most of us wish to write unpopular literature, because it is honourable to do so, we hope at the same time that its unpopularity will not be enough to prevent it from being sold, or at least from being published. Now art forms are subject to natural selection, and it is a matter of eventual fact that work which cannot be sold will not be written. Several factors are conspiring to increase the unpopularity of several fictional *genres* which could formerly hold their own—the economics of publishing, the disappearance of the audience to whom former novels were addressed, and the change of public taste.

The novel is a story with some reference to real life—which may be not more than a starting point. I think there are fundamentally only three kinds of novelistic story, special cases apart—three essences, if you like, which can be used to flavour it. There is the social novel, the prose equivalent of comedy or of tragedy, which makes its effect by appealing to our sympathy and experience of ourselves and our neighbours: there is the picaresque novel, which appeals to our need for adventure and rebellion—and there is the erotic novel, which appeals to our sexuality, with its shadow, the anterotic novel. The blends and permutations of these themes have been sufficient to sustain the novel as an art form through its whole development. There is a fourth, which is getting common, and which it is hard at times to avoid writing: that is the novel which is realistic, but the reality which it depicts is fantasy come to life and enacted in history. In our lifetime a writer possessed by a fantasy—the obsessive-compulsive fantasy of Kafka, for example, or the sadistic fantasy of Mirbeau—does not need to invent a situation in which it can be expressed; other similarly preoccupied people in positions of authority are already expressing these fantasies in current affairs. Kafka depicting his prison camp, digging his burrow, or trying to get into the castle is relying on his imagination, but today he could equally well be writing documentaries. Mirbeau's erotic torture does not now need to be set in the imaginary Orient. He could instead be writing recent history or biography, and I suspect he could find current documentary parallels within one day's flying-time of London.

The social ingredient in fiction is becoming harder and harder to use, because it depends to some extent on a settled state of society and values. People today read the social novels of the past. If in a contemporary setting one substitutes individual psychology for manners, the result approaches one of the other *genres* I have mentioned. The picaresque ingredient, in so far as it concerns adventure, particularly the adventures of rebels and masterless men, is again being overtaken by actuality—and actuality is more to the taste of modern readers.

The neotechnic society may very well have little interest in the social novel based on class or character. It seems quite possible that it will prefer to polarise its literary interests between actuality on one hand and romantic fantasy on the other. If so, Nordau's analogy with dancing will be more than apt, for the only social use which dancing retains, out of its many former uses, is erotic. That does not mean that society will be able to do without other serious art forms—on the Huxleyan pattern; it might well read the novels of the past, as we read the epic poetry of the past, and re-use them in its own tradition. But for anyone to write epic poetry today is evidence of a lack of literary judgment: the unpopular novel of today may be written tomorrow only as the analogue of morris-dancing.

Huxley's prediction was perceptive, because his Brave New World had nominally got rid both of psychopathology in private life and of psychopathology in office, albeit by means which reflect Huxley's own scepticism about the possibility of doing so. Future society with nuclear weapons must control both in fact if it is to survive at all, but its success may be partial only—the most frightening risk is that the fantastic-realistic *genre* of the future will go on being written in actual events, not ink, by deranged people who are enacting fantasy, instead of discharging it in literature.

The characteristically modern *genre* of fantastic is, I suppose, science fiction. This was originally no more than an imaginative forecast of the possibilities of science, but it has been captured by its literary ancestors in the same manner as the non-scientific romance, the erotic comic. At one extreme, it is not very different from that, with jargon playing the part of magic in pre-industrial fantasy, space travel as an exotic setting, and the mad scientist, who is a compound of Prometheus and Faust, playing the part of the wizard: one, that is, etymologically, contemptible for addiction to knowledge, as a drunkard is one contemptible for his addiction to drink, or a sluggard to sleep. At the other, it has become the vehicle through which more than one scientist who is not mad has tried to draw attention to the social activities of non-scientists who are.

There is no room here to pursue the ancestry of Utopias and of science fantasy turned satire—it begins, perhaps, with Lucian and with the *Golden Ass* and reaches us *via* More and Gulliver, but it stands in the same relation to comic-book science as *Candide* does to comic-book romance: both owe their sting to the convergence between fantasy and history. Just as Mirbeau and Kafka now sound unpleasantly factual, it is hard to tell whether some of the fantasies of science fiction are paranoiac or merely satirical—the slug-like invaders from outer Space who parasitise the will and intelligence by attaching themselves to the base of our skulls come from the same source as the electrical waves by means of which unseen enemies influence the certifiably insane—until we read that as a protection against their activities the U.S. Senate agrees to meet stripped to the waist,[64] and we find ourselves if not in real life at least close to it.

As I see it, the novel-writer today faces this problem: he has an audience which is increasingly demanding a literary separation of actuality and imagination, but he has also to cope with a triangular relationship between fiction as a vehicle for pure fantasy, fantasy-fiction as a vehicle for satire on society, and a society which is compelled by its leaders to enact pathological fantasies in fact. I have been talking about popular fiction—it may well be that those who wish to write unpopular fiction will opt out, and we shall have the same situation as exists in poetry, which now makes little attempt to address any audience outside the lecture room. There is a certain amount of self-satisfaction to be had from accepting the Third Programme as a ghetto, but the tenure of a literary form which lives on these terms is, to say the least, shaky.

One alternative is to write popular fiction. I think it is safe to say that there is no functioning art form, however poor its present execution, which cannot be exploited if one has enough ingenuity. And in any case the process is already in train. If the erotic-comic-book *genre* is growing up from below, the unpopular novel is coming down from above to meet it. Ever since Freud, *motif* has been gaining steadily at the expense of manner. The notion of writing 'popular' fiction as edification suggests the cleaned-up comic-book, in which, instead of secular bloodshed, David slaughters Goliath and Joan of Arc is burned at the stake. My intention here, though less specific than that, is more promising: if only the romance will be read, if motifs are to matter more than treatment, if literature is to be got in edgewise between them, at least the requirements are not more stringent than those stylisations which myth and ceremony imposed on Greek, or Elizabethan taste and politics on Tudor, drama. We need to study the natural history of literature today, not to acquire riches, or not only to acquire riches, but to accept the challenge which social

97

changes always impose on writers; when the philistine says 'You must', to reply 'I have—see how you like that!'

If I knew how to write the type of fiction which would fulfil these requirements today, I would write it—making the assumption which I have made here, that neurotic anxieties and immaturity are common property, but that my audience is saner than its censors and its leaders, and that the destructive emphases in literature, as well as in history, are to some extent imposed upon it. Godwin tried to do precisely this in *Caleb Williams* and *St. Leon*. If he did not make anarchism popular, at least he inspired Shelley. Graham Greene has attempted the same thing, but without using the crudely fetishistic techniques which the medium really demands. I would rather write like Longus than like Mr. Fleming, but if editors, readers or censors compel me to write like Mr. Fleming in order to be heard—or for that matter like the conformist colleagues of Pasternak—I would make a fair offer to turn any imposed restrictions into horrid arms against their originators.

Not all writers will share my assumptions. But most of them will recognise the symptoms I have described, the depletion, as it were, of the novel and the tendency for it to break up into its component literary *genres*. The novel has been the literary form par excellence of the period which gave us liberalism and science, but also industrialism and totalitarianism. How much it contributed as a social influence to these gains and losses I would not like to say. Any social influence it has had might now be transferred elsewhere. At the same time, as long as stories are read, regardless of what is in them, fiction is still a possible medium.

If, moreover, like so many good people, we are depressed by popular literature today, or by some of the alarming things in it, we should remember that Prometheus is not only the symbol of cruelty, and Faustian competition to enact the fantasies of deranged people is not the only function of science. Shelley's answer is the right one. Science has made it possible for us to understand some of the relations between psychosymbolism in literature and behaviour in society, or at least to look for them. It has also, by the same token, made it possible to envisage turning psychopathology out of history, whether or not we can or should turn it out of literature. What we require is the will. And if indeed the audiences for whom we write are saner than their leaders, and saner than their literature, the writer today, like the doctor and the psychiatrist, has a duty of incitement as well as consolation—for, in Tatius' terms, if Herakles can unbind Prometheus we will not have to worry about the misfortunes of virtue.

V

The Naked Lady

Unfortunately, psychoanalysis has less to say about beauty than about most things. All that seems certain is that it originates in sexual sensibility. The love of beauty is a perfect example of a sentiment whose aim has been inhibited. Beauty and allure are first of all attributes of sexual objects. It is remarkable that the genitalia themselves, the sight of which is always sexually exciting, are hardly even regarded as beautiful; beauty seems to accrue rather to certain secondary sexual characteristics.

SIGMUND FREUD

THIS year, which has seen Parliament still trying to settle what books adult Englishmen should be allowed to read, has brought us the first openly-available picture book[65] of the erotic sculptures of the tenth century Hindu temples of Konarak, in Orissa, and Khajuraho, in Vindya Pradesh. These temple carvings have not contributed to our taste—only to the erotic-exotic myth, through missionary-borne hints of depravity and the visits of officers' parties, while their women watched jugglers or bought souvenirs. If anything about them embarrasses us now, it ought to be our past behaviour—mitigated by the highly creditable part played by other Englishmen in preserving the works themselves from Indian apathy and Victorian fanaticism. The odd oversight which left Latin and Greek in our curricula has meant that no precautions have ever quite managed to cut us off from literatures which celebrate the physical experience of sexuality. It has been much easier to keep us in ignorance of the chief artistic tradition which celebrates it visually, giving it the place occupied in our own iconography by the celebration of pain.

Macaulay greeted Hindu art with ignorant disgust. We are more likely to greet it with equally ignorant enthusiasm. This is an art for which we have no parallel. It raises questions about the use and place of the human response to sexual representations in art for which we have no critical answers, but are on the verge of having to find some. It does not very much matter whether Mulk-Raj Anand's selection represents the best of Hindu sculpture as a whole (it does not, but that can be seen elsewhere) or even whether it represents the best of that part of the tradition which our prejudices separate as 'erotic'; there is no other basis for selecting these temples in two different styles and hundreds of miles apart. A Chinese of the Empire would have set up a separate and equally valid category for European pictures of women with bare feet. Sri Anand's commentary is not itself particularly instructive—it makes no attempt, for instance, to relate the iconography of love in these sculptures to the parallel literary tradition. But the book still represents a break-through, even though it must make the obligatory gesture by being, at seven guineas, too dear for 'ordinary people' to buy.

'Ordinary people' who buy art books for pleasure and information would in fact get much more of both from Phaidon's wider but more reticent *Art of India*. The gestures of Hindu figures are symbols to remind us of what we know but do not see. The gesture of price is of this order. It reminds us that other 'ordinary people', who never look at Hindu or any other art by intention, would look at this, because of its subject, 'for the wrong reasons'; and their betters must ensure that they do not do so by making it, at seven guineas, too expensive for them. I will take this gesture as my text.

The trade mark of our ethical and religious tradition is the rejection, and the exclusion from art, not of sexuality, but of genitality. Contraband in any form has by critical agreement an extremely low aesthetic, as well as moral, prestige. For Roger Fry the *maithuna* groups, the ecstatic lovers who are a recurrent symbol of Hindu iconography, like the dying God of Near-Eastern religions, are intrinsically inaesthetic—they introduce an 'irrelevant' interest. The shock-effect of such groups on Europeans is a cultural accident, certainly—it was no part of the artist's intention to produce shock—but not more irrelevant than the shock-effect on Asians of a first encounter with the sadistic topics of Christian iconography: these have little empathy for us, and are now barely decorative, but that is because our attitudes were made by the tradition, and the imagery reflects them. The emotions produced by the depiction of coition in Indian temples and of execution in ours are in fact homologous, though antipodal—any shock effect of Hindu art on us is essential to its intention, which is to idealise genital pleasure as we idealise death and barrenness. We have no right to avoid this intention, still less to brush it off as figurative so that we can treat the tradition in our own critical terms. I imagine Asians have similar difficulty with an iconography in which mother and child are the conventional emblem of virginity, but asceticism and self-torment are not new religious themes to them; while European taste has banished genital sexuality altogether, and art like that of Khajuraho faces it with the task of regrowing a self-amputated limb.

In one sense the lopsidedness of our art is really fictitious, for the impression created by our libraries and galleries is false. Painting and literature which celebrate physical sexuality as Stubbs celebrates horses, or Surtees hunting, are not absent from our experience because artists had no inclination to produce them, or because there was no demand for them, but because they have been concealed, prohibited or destroyed by an active minority determined to see we did not get them. A whole segment of art, literature, and even everyday speech has been deleted, against the will and the real *mores* of our culture. We need only compare the songs which Cecil Sharp published with those he actually collected[66] to see how extensive this extraordinary phenomenon has been. Contact with work like the Konarak friezes is only part of the gradual and quite recent breaching of the screen set up by the prohibitors against cultures with which they could not tamper.

It has sometimes been implied by Western critics that taboos apart coition, like eating, is an inherently poor visual subject for purely artistic reasons, and that it is only tolerable in Indian art for the reasons of religious significance which make equally inaesthetic Christian symbols tolerable in our own. This, I think, is Englishmanship, for the most serious of the available non-Indian examples—in Greek vase painting, or in Roman Arretine moulded pottery reliefs, for instance—show the exact opposite. I would have thought, it is in fact the prototypic activity, combining empathy and figure-tension, which the struggling, balanced or 'emerging' figures of Baroque suggest: and that they owe their effect very largely to this erotic suggestion. A whole range of sculpture from Rodin to abstraction is patently reaching out, in the tensions it creates, to the formal pattern of the 'primal scene'. The explicit use of this in Hindu art is nevertheless unique—other cultures have produced erotic figures, from Roman lamp designs to netsuké, but none so much, nor of such quality.

I do not think there have been many periods in our history when under conditions of a free market erotic literature and art would have failed to find distinguished producers or to fulfil a legitimate need of audiences. A surprisingly large number of writers and artists, even in the great ages of decency, have at some time ignored the cultural prohibition, even when they kept their work to themselves, and many more such works must have been destroyed by their authors, or, like Turner's sketches, Burton's diaries, Byron's autobiography and Swinburne's *facetiae*, by embarrassed relatives or executors.

In our culture most people do not expect, and are not expected, to express themselves in any form of imaginative art unless it is their occupation to do so. But people who neither draw nor produce 'literature' for its own sake will do so under the influence of sufficiently strong motives, as sceptics will pray involuntarily, and of these motives for self-expression, sexuality and anxieties connected with it appear to have the lowest threshold. The only circumstance which popularly excuses the attempt of unpoetic people to write poetry is being in love. In the same way sexual fantasy is now almost the only topic which excites unliterary people to write what is, in fact, imaginative prose, or to produce imaginative drawings.

Indeed, partly as a result of prohibition, art which deals with the theme of sexual satisfaction, recollected, anticipated or imagined, is probably the only thematic art for which, if it were available, there now would be a consistent and general demand in our society—wide enough to perform the unimaginable and restore contact between artists and the general public. Those who doubt this need only study the natural history of advertisement. In the act of replying that they 'have no wish', like Roebuck Ramsden, 'for that kind of notoriety', artists must themselves be aware that people have only recently been required to like art for the Right Reasons—indeed only clever ones have managed to do so, and most of its past development has depended upon giving its patrons the ikons, the portraits of Borgias and racehorses, and the ornamental saltcellars which they wanted for the wrong reasons.

It is perfectly true that not much of the *clandestine* erotic art of the past or present—there is a vast collection of such material in the research archives of Kinsey's laboratory in Indiana—is of outstanding merit. Much of it is extremely tiresome or of pathological interest only. But one would expect the quality of art to depend at least in part upon the tolerance afforded to it. Almost all our sexually preoccupied art, as well as our sexually preoccupied science, is compulsive. It reflects anxiety rather than celebration, and it is this anxiety which generates the energy behind the composition. When the stage was a prohibited occupation, plays were commonly poor and actors commonly rogues— art which involves, like prostitution, a gesture of social defiance is apt either to exhibit the damaging strain and exertion which we find in Henry Miller, or to be produced only by artists driven, as Verlaine was, by a major personality disorder. Moreover, sexual allusion has become to the modern audience not so much indecent as incongruous, which is a far greater handicap to artistic treatment. We have to control our sense of incongruity in approaching the temple sculptures, as we do in approaching Chinese music. Folk poetry, and work like that of Burns or Béranger which is effectively folk poetry, can take this particular incongruity in its stride. It is only in the last few years that more pretentious writing has been able to do so, at least in this country.

The natural history of sexual satisfaction is now in fact, as we have seen, reappearing steadily as a topic in English literature at all levels from the successors of *Bulldog Drummond* to *Room at the Top*. We are becoming able to observe and use this long-prohibited section of everyday experience as Lawrence could not— that is, naturally and without strain. Visual art is a tougher proposition—(I suspect, from the work of Resnais and others, that its natural vehicle will now turn out to be the film)—the cultural ban through Europe has in this case been more uniform: we have fewer precedents, and Hindu traditions are too deeply set in their cultural context to provide models. We might usefully look at them, however, to find out the functions of such art—since even Parliament concedes that it has functions. They constitute one of the most interesting parts of the biology of aesthetics, and may well be a special need of our present form of society.

The art of Khajuraho and Konarak is primarily didactic. It is by intention a spiritual exhibition. What is presented is an experience, edifying, practical and symbolic, of the way of Release which is the Hindu ideal, embodied in one form of Release, the contemplation of art. Another mode of Release is the experience of sexual ecstasy. The lovers both celebrate and demonstrate the means of this: at the same time, because of the power of sexual imagery to excite physical response, they set our search for it in motion, to be taken home, as it were—as a flower show stimulates our wish to have gardens.

The religious background of the temple images is confusing to a European, and, apparently, to many Indians. Figures of this kind occur widely in India, but the concentration of genital imagery at these two sites is unusually high. Sri Anand mentions the Kaula sect as being associated with the temples. These were 'left-hand' Sakta—devotees, roughly, of the Shavian-Bergsonian Life Force in its benign aspect, considered as female and active (Sakti, prakrti) as opposed to male and immanent (Siva, purusa), and embodied symbolically and actually in women. If we look up Kaula practice in European books we shall find it described as 'the worst result of the worst superstitious ideas that have ever disgraced and degraded the human race'[67]—we know better than to expect from this a larger-scale Inquisition, or mass human sacrifices like those of the Aztecs or the Benin kings, for the hysterical tone identifies the subject: the Kaula apparently did no more than practise in private *stripuja* (woman worship) involving ritual promiscuity and taboo-breaking, and the Five Sacraments (mākaras)—wine, flesh, fish, ritual gesture (or according to another interpretation, dried grain) and *maithuna*

—or, if we prefer it, 'offering to women the so-called homage of sensual love and carnal passion, wholly regardless of social rules and restrictions'. They seem to have confined their devotion strictly to the goddess as Eros, leaving the more acceptable celebration of her aspect as Thanatos to the blood-offerings of the semi-orthodox *Durga-puja*, and to sects like those of the Kirati (hook-swingers) who celebrated her masochistically. Kaula-ism was not much more popular with later Hindu orthodoxy than with Victorian indologists, largely because its love-feast violated caste barriers by considering all initiates as Brahmanas so long as the ceremony lasted, regardless of their usual status.

Much of the practice of Indian and Chinese sexual mysticism is complicated by the medically inaccurate belief that the semen must be conserved to nourish the soul, which led to a gymnastic avoidance of ejaculation, and by attempts to enhance the symbolic and esoteric significance of coition as a type of the union of Logos and Energy, Mind and the Void, and so on. The Kaula scriptures distinguish rigidly between the true enjoyment of the Enlightened and the secular pleasures of the uninitiated (pasu, 'beasts'), who are 'mere enjoyers of women'. There seems to be little to identify either the Kaula or the stylised sexual ikons of the Tāntrists with the fashionable *nayikas* and maidens of the sculptures. Some other Hindu sects, particularly among the cults of Krishna, followed Vallabha's teaching that asceticism formed no part of holiness and made less attempts to find esoteric justifications for sexual pleasure, regarding it as good and edifying in itself, part of the *pusti-marga* (way of prosperity). This seems closer to the abandon of the temple friezes. However, ritual *maithuna* apart, the general tradition of Tāntrik ideas, both in India and in China, does imply that the divine is embodied in every woman, and that sexual intercourse, while it might have special merit for spiritual experts, was a secular sacrament conferring both physical and moral virtue—'buddhatvam yosidyonisamāsritam'—enlightenment is in the sexual parts of Woman: the dictum is attributed to the Buddha Sākyamuni, who 'conquered buddhahood by the practice of Tāntrik rites in his Harim'.[68] The ideal of *brahmācārya*, which Westerners and some Indians have taken to imply sexual abstinence, is equally capable of being taken to mean the psychoanalyst's ideal, freedom from *compulsive* behaviour.

The Naked Lady

A prime interest, if not the prime interest, of oriental mystics in sexual experience is that it can be used as a tool to produce the state or phenomenon which the Tāntrists called *sunya*—loss of personal identity, 'void'—the oceanic feeling of non-existence which is a general aim of yogic techniques. This state is embedded in the usual symbolism—in the Buddhist Tāntrika system *sunya* is identified with the female; she represents, among other things, the oblivion and wellbeing of the womb, of the child asleep, the fantasy of being 'swallowed up', and the submergence of identity at the moment of orgasm ('la mort doulce') rolled into one. Saiva-Tāntrika, which was the Kaula and the Temple-builders' version, makes the Void and pure intellect male (Siva) and dynamic and creative reality female (Sakti), though one face of Siva's total manifestation is itself female. (Blake's home-made version of Hinduism, since we are on the subject, follows the same two myths: Ahala is to Urizen as Vāmadeva Umā is to Siva Tatpurusa—she is his *anima*, the 'feminine indolent bliss', but she is also *sunya*, 'the passive, idle sleep, the enormous night and darkness of Death'—once separated from him she 'wanders sleepless on the margin of Non-entity': whereas Enitharmon, escaped from the body of Los, becomes his *sakti* and weaves him willy-nilly in her looms. Blake makes the Freudian point in so many words—

The nature of a Female Space is ... that it shrinks the Organs of Life till they become Finite and itself Infinite.)

The interest of all this to us is less in the ideas behind it, or even its possible connection with the intentions of temple art, than in the fact that the associated practices have a definite relevance to our understanding of aesthetic biology. Sexual orgasm is the only ecstatic phenomenon in common experience, and it does indeed involve a death-like loosening of our grip on personal identity. The Indian mystics, like the European Adamites, disgusted our ancestors by introducing sex under cover of esoteric experience—we might now be more inclined to wonder whether the boot is not on the other foot—whether we have been talking esoteric prose all our lives, and whether religion and philosophy which pursue ecstatic states are not in search of substitutes for, or sophistications of, the physiological version.

107

There are some biological grounds for thinking that the same applies to art, or at least to that art which generates intense affect, the individualist art of our tradition. Orgasm is the most intense human aesthetic experience, taking 'aesthetic' in its literal meaning —a more concentrated version of the oblivious exaltation which artists sometimes get from the act of composition, and audiences rather less commonly from the act of appreciation. In fact, rather than argue how far art is an expression of aim-inhibited sexuality, we might find it more profitable to consider how far sexual experience can be a form of art, in the sense we now attach to that word. The Indians so regarded it; I strongly suspect that in our culture it is about to become one, and that it may prove superior to others in discharging much of the activity which goes into the typically individualistic art we know. This is yet another case where the intelligence of Aldous Huxley's predictions in *Brave New World* outran his morale in dealing with them. There seem to be a number of grounds on which one could argue—and Aldous Huxley should not have blamed the Brave New Worlders for arguing—that erotic experience is a direct appeal to the original of our aesthetic sense, and erotic art is propaganda for it. This seems a long way from Roger Fry and his irrelevant interest—it does not, of course, devalue art, for we can have both women *and* Beethoven, since it is the genius of human appreciation that it can make new values for itself by elaborating physiological originals. Nor does it replace the social functions of art, of which our society makes no use. But *la fouterie est le lyrisme du peuple* in a perfectly literal sense, and those who show interest in it may be demanding art for more nearly the 'right' reason than those who pursue more complicated esoteric merits. As to the carefully-elaborated satisfaction of the spiritual connoisseur, or the oceanic feeling of the mystic,

'What is it, who can tell?'

We could make a plausible case for believing that in prestige-free restatement, it is

no more
than thou and I have done before
with Bridget and with Nell!

I suspect that excursions into Hindu religious symbolism are

108

in any case more likely to make a European observer of the temple sculpture miss than discover the point. He will be encouraged by those modern Indians who are defensive over their tradition, through infection with our prudery, to explain away the sensual invitation in transcendental terms. The surasundaris, fair women of the gods, are symbolic messengers who show us the attributes of the Mother Goddess and invite us to her. But so does every naked woman, even in a tradition of art which has insisted that we mutilate or falsify her anatomy. The lovers' hands are certainly set in symbolic postures to remind us of attributes of gods and of the world, but their bodies remind us of our wives and lovers. They incite, approve, and instruct.

This, I suggest, is what secular erotic art would do in our own culture if disturbed people did not prevent it. The appeal of literary and artistic presentation of sexual activity is only confined to the 'corrupt', or their modern cousins, the 'immature', if human beings generally are corrupt and immature. Large numbers of people want it (if they did not, such energy would not have to be spent in prohibiting it) for reasons as honourable as those which make hunters read the novels of Surtees—plus one other, its power to produce psychophysical excitement directly. This is the factor the prohibitors emphasise, because they are upset by their own response to it—they represent it as socially dangerous and artistically unworthy, preferring art to exploit the only other theme which gives an equally strong physical reaction, namely, violence. Love is corrupting, shameful and dangerous—violence, as we have seen, is wholesome and cathartic, besides being politically useful.

Incitement is inherent in all art which 'celebrates' human pleasures, and a wholly worthy artistic aim. But although people certainly do seek out sexual art to experience excitement, in our society they seek it equally for information and for reassurance. Part of the popularity of sexual literature today is due to the widespread conviction that knowledge is being kept from us which would make for greater proficiency and enjoyment in our own experience. Part is the result of legitimate curiosity, the desire to compare our own habits and performance with those of others, and be liberated by reassurance from the reservations and rigidities which alloy our release with anxiety.

Visual erotic art has a special and deeper significance, for it acts directly on the human response to sexual dimorphism—that biologically extraordinary group of reactions to the sight of the external genitalia which evolution has promoted to be the chief determinant of human sexual and social behaviour. Reassurance against the castration fear may well be the original motive of representational art, and the manufacture of amulets for that purpose the oldest function of figure-carving. It is this function which has made the artist the traditionally-licensed *voyeur*—it is an important, perhaps the chief, source of his power, as well as the basis of the oddly selective modesties he has been obliged to observe in different cultures; and it is possibly behind many other aesthetic phenomena—the flight of modern sculpture into non-representational techniques, for example. Hindu temple art is in this sense didactic, or therapeutic, quite apart from the special part which genital symbolism plays in its belief. The temple builders capitalised these human Oedipal responses as a source of energy—we do likewise, but in a reverse sense; their ideology got its motive power from the resolution of the Oedipal fear, ours from the anxiety which it generates. Permission and incitement to carry a similar freedom into everyday sexual life are the precautions they had to take to preserve that arrangement against individual doubts—censorship and the maintenance of private sexual anxiety are our precautions to preserve the contrary adjustment against individual wishes. It is a peaceful revenge of the temple builders that a modern European biologist or psychiatrist may be more spiritually at ease with the iconography of Khajuraho or of Bhuvaneshwar than that of Chartres, and more able to give his intellectual assent to the four faces of Siva and the beauty of the Apsaras than to the virgins and thaumaturgists of our own religious art; imagery which he cannot help recognising as emotionally mischievous, coupled to a confusion between symbol and historicity which assaults his mental integrity.

The literary counterpart of the tenth-century temple sculptures is the body of Sanskrit didactic poems on sexual technique as a polite accomplishment, which extend from antiquity to the mid-sixteenth century, and circulate in vernacular versions up to the present day. Their content does not square exactly with that of the temple friezes: in general they tend to be more restrictive, particularly towards orogenital activities, which temple art treats with enthusiasm—the stylised *mignardises* are the same, however. Unlike Chinese and Arab erotic manuals, they owe nothing to personal experience and much to a Brahmanic mania for ritualisation and classification—alongside some brilliantly practical advice they contain long passages of fossil material, repeating for two millennia that the women of this region are to be won by blows, and the women of that region are slow in love. The matter is uniquely Indian—the typology of man and woman, astrological calendars for the wooing of woman according to her build, postural variants in coition, many of them derived from *Hatha-yoga* (the Wise Parrot of the *Dinālāpanikā-Sukasaptati* describes fifty-three in detail and dozens more by name only): some of these suggest that the sculptural need to depict the *maithuna* couples standing may have 'fed back' into secular practice. Stranger by our standards are the named varieties of nail-scratches, hair-pulling, toothmarks, erotic blows, and sounds with which the beloved replies to them. (As a measure of the compilatory origin of these poems, even the earliest are in some confusion whether these excitatory blows are to be given with actual instruments or with hand-*mudras* named after the shears, the wedge, and so on—Yasodhara condemns the more literal interpretation as dangerous, and lists a number of accidents.) Odd, perhaps—yet this apparent dissipation of aggressive behaviour in the play-function of sex had probably its own place in the economy: the extreme stylisation serves to control it. Unlike sexual violence in our own literature it remains play; love-play, too, not hate, for the chief feature of all Indian erotic writing is its conspicuous tenderness.

By contrast with our own semi-erotic literature, in which the woman is expendable, or behaves like a male-dictated fantasy, these books are devoted to instructing men in the technique of satisfying real women. They assume that all women can be given the experience of sexual pleasure if only one knows how. To that end a gentleman (the nayīka of Sanskrit literature is closer to rendering all the meanings of 'gentleman' than almost any other) must study her tastes, her physical and temperamental make-up, the customs of all the diverse cultures in the subcontinent from which she may come, the places where she should be touched, the sounds of pleasure or displeasure she may make, the degree of passion, violence or gentleness she will expect, and all the techniques, usual or exceptional, which can make sure that her experience of pleasure is complete. It may be that this is the way to satisfaction for himself, but if so he is perceptive enough to see that:

> Suvarnanābha writes—the girl's own grain matters more than local usage—be flexible with her taste, and from one time to another. Love by local convention won't satisfy her if her needs are different. Techniques and whims, too, must alter for special occasions as they do from country to country. You must be able to deal with both.
>
> (*Kandarpacūdāmani* II 5, 26/28)

It is pathognomonic that our culture speaks of 'whores' tricks' when Suvarnanābha would have called them husbands' tricks. The husband's experience of release is no more compromised by this need to take thought than the artist's is compromised by the requirements of form and of his medium. 'When the wheel of love begins to turn there are no more precepts', but it is his duty to ensure by art that it does turn, holding back his own orgasm as necessary by controlling his breath, repeating the syllable 'om', which stands for tranquillity and self-mastery, and meditating on the cobra-hooded, tortoise-throned Visnu; as we in similar circumstances might think hard about the Archbishop of Canterbury.

The Freudian insight, while it has made sexual behaviour comprehensible, has tended to put a pathological valuation on all extragenital behaviour which mammalian studies do not support. It has also made us forget how far sexual pleasure is a skill which can be taught. Our society has no functionary charged with promoting sexual satisfaction. If it can develop a literature of sexuality as explicitly devoted to enjoyment as that of ballroom dancing the gain in sincerity alone will be of value. Reading the *Ratirahasya* or the *Kandarpacūdāmani* (which we may do, unless we understand Sanskrit,[69] only in a mixture of German and Latin) we may regret that they are too far from our culture to be worth disseminating with paper backs. We have pallider equivalents, produced under the convention that enjoyment may be encouraged if the encouragement passes for moral or mental hygiene—it must smell of incense or of carbolic, and it must not be more than ordinarily pleasant. There is an advantage in turning to poetry for the *dharma* of sexual behaviour, but at the moment the business of information and reassurance lies chiefly with biological science.

Most artists are not, of course, concerned primarily with public health, and some people may doubt whether sexual satisfaction has anything to do with the imparting or receiving of information. The public, which welcomes all the information it can get, and the erotic writers of older cultures, would probably not share these doubts. In our own culture the mere fact of imparting information, if it carries with it the sense of permission, that there is nothing to be afraid of, can be a valuable reassurance. The steady disappearance from private habits of the long-standing taboo upon orogenital contacts and upon masturbation, which figure largely in the temple friezes, seems to be directly due to reassurance from biology and psychology. Indeed, the actual content of sexual behaviour probably changes much less between cultures than the individual's capacity to enjoy it without guilt.

The final point of the analogy between sexual experience and our typical, non-social type of artistic activity, is medical, or at least therapeutic, and suggests an answer to a question we asked earlier on, about the hygienic value of art. We know that violence in contemporary literature, or 'abnormality' in modern art generally, is said by some people to discharge aggressive and other impulses which would otherwise appear in behaviour, and is therefore valuable (they instance the striking improvement in civilised manners compared with eighteenth-century England or gladiatorial Rome, where little aggression appears in art)—others, like Dr. Wertham,[70] hold that if we bring our children up from an early age on the contemplation of paraphilia and brutality we shall encourage it by example. (These two views are probably not incompatible.) Both artistic and sexual activity appear to involve, or to be able to accommodate, controlled regression and controlled aggression; both terminate, when effective, in *moksa*, release—accompanied, in the case of sexuality, by a violent and beneficial neuro-physical discharge. If it were true that Oedipal anxieties and neurotic matter generally could

really be 'discharged' either in art or in the conscious development of erotic behaviour, the discovery would be highly important.

Present clinical experience tells in the opposite sense, however,
and reverses the priorities—our art and our erotic capability are
both handicapped *because* of the investment of our mental energies in residual paraphilias and at infantile levels—we do not
need to develop satisfactory art and sex to cure ourselves of
immaturity, but to cure ourselves of immaturity in order that
our art and sex may be satisfactory. This is undoubtedly true,
and so far as major disorders are concerned, clinically evident—
compulsive homosexuality or flagellomania are not cured by
practising them. The difficulty arises from the extent to which
our clinical experience is culture-limited. Both the normal and
the possible have been heavily influenced, in our definition, by living in a culture fundamentally antagonistic to genitality; this
attitude, which is itself a paraphilic manifestation, does not
strengthen the power of individuals, especially if they are already
handicapped, to opt for mature genital interests. The emphases
which we find most intractable when we try to cure them appear,
fully-absorbed, in the practice of other times and places—
homosexuality in Greece and Japan, transvestism in certain Red
Indian peoples, public nudity in others (can one 'suffer from'
exhibitionism in Dinka culture, where neither sex wear clothes?)
or the incorporation into costume and custom, at one time or
another, of all the most frequent fetishes. 'I do wish,' said one
therapist, after wrestling for several months with an isolated but
particularly intractable symptom of this kind, 'that he'd go and
live where they *all* do it—but then no doubt there would be
something else.'

The essential difference, if I had to define it, between a 'sexual
technique' and a paraphilic compulsion is that the second is
associated with anxiety, while the first is not. We do not need to
draw a superficial conclusion from this variety. Customs are the
product of local adjustment—the bushman can walk barefoot on
broken glass, because his feet are adjusted to going bare, while
ours are not. The real point is that our culture, and others like it,
is a babel of competing needs and personalities unparalleled in
the small, accurately-balanced tribal and city orders of the past.

Extreme misplacements and personality disorders can resist exorcism in art, and will probably be incapable of 'discharge' in sexual behaviour or anywhere else; others, like erotic murder or cannibalism, can never become socially acceptable as such in our culture, even if they are tolerated elsewhere. But it may quite possibly prove that the widening of the permitted range of behaviour which we have begun to acquire from the knowledge of other cultures will be able to deal with all but the tail of the distribution. Apart from anything else, it steadily reduces the number of manifestations which give rise to disturbance secondarily—if orogenital activities are not 'abnormal' unless they swamp all other sexual behaviour, and not discreditable in any case, they will not disturb their owners and present as foci of guilt, marital strife, and even murder—which, until recently, they did. If predominant homosexuality were tolerated, it would be a disability but not a cause of suicide. A Roman psychiatrist would not have undertaken to treat Ovid on the basis of his remark that on the whole he was less interested in boys than in women— any more than a modern one would treat a Papuan for eating his mother instead of burying her, or an ancient Chinese for lighting incense on his wife's abdomen and pricking her with needles as an erotic stimulus: with an Englishman in the same situation, the social significance at least would be different, though the unconscious significance might well be the same.

It is not, moreover, with 'cases' that we are here concerned, so much as with the general tone and direction of the culture in which the 'cases' occur. The development of sexual experience over the next century, unless present trends are reversed, is likely to be more permissive and more genitally orientated; and 'normal', or permitted, expression at the same time more and more polymorphous. It is a pure guess what effect this widening will have on non-sexual expressions of immaturity or on its quasi-sexual expression in art. My guess, which is that of a biologist, not a psychoanalyst, is that it will affect them for the better, though it may leave some unchanged (one consequence, in a culture where upbringing is so highly diverse, will be to increase even more the importance of temperamental 'matching' between sexual partners for all but the most adaptable; the

Sanskrit writers, cataloguing the geographical and ethnic varia-
tions in custom and taste, warned the student not to imagine
that any of the techniques which they teach are uniformly acceptable to women of all cultures, or even to all women in any one
culture: moreover, the expert should be perfectly familiar with
national costumes and accents so as not to be caught out by
visiting expatriates. In our case, however, where personalities
cover an enormous range, there is not even the possibility of
geographical classification to help us).

If any one more general neurotic preoccupation now 'discharged' in art is capable of total discharge in sexual play, I
would expect it to be precisely our characteristic preoccupation
with violence—particularly if, like sadomasochistic phenomena
generally, it is to a large extent built by accretion round a frustrated
desire for intensity of sexual experience. This does not mean that
our coital behaviour will necessarily become, even symbolically,
more violent, or more like our present reading-matter, or that it
will cultivate the peculiarities of Indian erotology, though when
summer dresses are worn one can see in the London Under-
ground examples of *nakhacchedya* worthy of any Indian beauty—
the discharge may well be equally if not better obtained for many
people through an intensity of a different sort, more nearly
approaching the contemplative *moksa* of the sects. This, if it
were to happen, would certainly not be the equivalent of a
complete therapeutic analysis for the whole culture, but its social
effects might nevertheless be striking.

It follows, if so, that since aggression and sex are now the
chief components of popular art, the larger part of that art could
be, and may be, replaced, exactly as Aldous Huxley predicted, by
the cultivation of increasingly elaborate sexual experience by
'ordinary' people, as soon as they have the privacy, the reassurance, and the contraceptive technique necessary for the purpose.
In contrast to Huxley, it will be the comics rather than Beethoven
that this process is likely to displace. It may well better our
general taste, and at the same time reintroduce us to the idea of
passionate tenderness, which we have almost entirely lost in
literature and art.

Some people will no doubt ask whether 'ordinary' citizens wish to make their sexual experience varied rather than uneventfully satisfactory, and whether the demand for variety is not itself a sign of the immature. As a concealed value-judgment with which to intimidate questioners, maturity has taken over the function discharged in the past by 'normality', 'decency', and the 'natural', and we should recognise it as such. Other people may wonder whether such an emphasis on variety has another basis: since elaboration of this kind has a social distribution (correlated not unnaturally with leisure, privacy, central heating and running water) in encouraging 'variety' upper-level counsellors are simply encouraging conformity to their own tastes. One answer to both objections seems to me to be that the justification of erotics resembles the justification of high-class cookery and musical appreciation, both 'educated' tastes, which are most enthusiastically propagated by people who have found them worthwhile in terms of their own enjoyment. We have elaborated orchestral music because we have made demands on it which no previous culture has made; we have elaborated cookery as a source of individual pleasure. Tastes in variety vary—a programme or a menu, after all, is only an opportunity, not a command. The analogy to other aesthetic elaborations—food and wine, for example—is fully maintained in practice; the ascetic rejects them all, the Puritan insists upon plain wholesome food free of demoralising Persian apparatus (if he is a left-wing Puritan he will substitute 'natural' for 'plain'). In this case, however, there is the added justification that the sexual equivalent of good wholesome food, defined by philosophies which resent the necessity to eat at all, is not a universally adequate diet.

Art and literature can contribute to the essential process of reassurance if they are able to describe human natural history without anxiety: this is precisely what the Sanskrit erotic literature does, in spite of its elaborate conventions. At no time has humanity been better placed to avail itself of this function of art. The 'grey disease' is certainly not cured in our culture, and there are deplorable new foci of it in the Marxist world which threaten to infect previously immune parts of Asia. But if the remission holds, we may find ourselves the first culture that has ever been fully able to realise the potential play-function of sexuality, for we may at any moment get reliable control over our fertility. It will be a fair exchange for the knowledge of erotic art if modern India draws equal though different benefits from that discovery.

Once this occurs, I suggest that a very large part of our present 'aesthetic' behaviour will be diverted into a new channel. Meanwhile, creative artists are the professional makers of amulets—of objects wanted for the Wrong Reasons. Many are unhappy upon more than egalitarian grounds at letting literature become a hieratic language like Sanskrit, while the public reads books and magazines on an unprecedented scale—in accepting the lecture hall, the intellectual ghetto, and the artistic Establishment which wants art for the Right Reasons, as their natural audience. The erotic function of art is one which might conceivably let them out—among the pin-ups, the films and the comics, it is true, which are amulets of a less worthy kind, but also among live people, who want art for the wrong reasons: it might even preserve them from the ossifying Brahmanism which appears to have destroyed the older Indian societies. More significantly, too, for our generation, psychoanalysis suggests that the erotic interest in life is the most likely preservative of our current will to hit back at the devotees of the Goddess's other face, both in art and in public affairs, who are working with such unflagging zeal to celebrate Death finally and at our expense.

VI

On Laying Plato's Ghost

Judging from the hideous ornaments, and the equally
hideous music, admired by most savages, it might be urged
that their aesthetic faculty was not so highly developed as
in certain animals, for instance, in birds.

> CHARLES DARWIN: *Descent of Man*

Beauty is an arbitrary Advantage, and depends upon
Custom and Fancy.

> JEREMY COLLIER: *A short View of the Immorality and
> Profaneness of the English Stage* (1698)

I ONCE spent a wet seaside holiday in complete contentment,
playing paper doyleys on a pianola. Now doyleys are not
designed to be played, but if they are symmetrical they will in
fact play a tune of sorts—or at least make a noise which is symmetrical and non-random.

Imagine that this practice has spread, so that only designs which
produced satisfactory tunes are marketable. In this case it is possible to predict that all doyleys will soon be playable—as the
result of natural selection. The makers might not intend this
result, nor be aware of the exact use to which the doyleys were
being put, and which was determining their popularity. Of course,
if they were aware, and were also familiar with the structure of a
pianola, they could guarantee the marketability of their product
either by design or by empirical testing. But an unusually perceptive doyley-maker might arrive at the spacing of the holes in
a pianola without knowledge that such instruments exist, and

solely on the evidence of sales. This could lead him to formulate a set of aesthetic 'laws of nature'—that the sale of doyleys depends on certain recurrent mathematical relationships in the spacing of holes, that these patterns had a quantal basis, and that in circular doyleys the popularity-factor was related to the number of axes of symmetry.

A scientific doyley-maker might at this point guess, if not the truth, at least something not far off it: a less scientific but equally intellectual doyley-maker would begin to invoke entelechies, inherent principles and Divine artistry, and from such beginnings an entire neo-Pythagorean edifice might very easily arise, with an edifying cast to it. Before we could say 'Aquinas' the Jesuits would be telling us 'that there are those for whom, in some inscrutable sense, the way to God lies through the holes in a doyley', and some of us would be suitably impressed.

Objects which contain non-random arrays of great complexity do occur in nature—some result from simple properties of matter: others are far more complex productions which either convey or express biological information. There is strong reason to believe that these have arisen, like the saleable doyleys, by the action of selection on random variation. None of them resembles a piece of music in having as its only function the satisfaction of human aesthetic sense, but many do satisfy it, though it is often very difficult to say exactly why. Association and symbolism play a large part—perception of form, especially form which is just too complex to be analysed as it is perceived, is another component —others, like the sense of balance and proportion, may be som-aesthetic and our response to them an abortive movement. Oddly enough, there is virtually no criticism of natural objects to parallel the criticism of art—possibly the critic feels that his remarks are wasted on objects which can neither be pleased, nor offended, nor even altered by them: the field is left swept and garnished for the psychologist.

It seems a reasonable guess that if the rest of human behaviour is adaptive in origin, the human perception of beauty is so too, and that unlike the pianola it has been formed by the regularities available to it—those, naturally, which man is able to detect, because there are plenty that he cannot. He is well equipped to appreciate, for example, harmonic relations and spatial symmetry, but not polarisation. The visual evidences of Divine artistry which theologians would quote if they were insect theologians, and had compound eyes sensitive to ultra-violet, would be quite different. So would their arts—they would take no interest in sculpture, but they would share our liking for circular, radially-disposed and symmetrical objects (which would remind them of food, the physiological origin of much of their social behaviour, exactly as many objects have for us a genital symbolism and remind us of sex, which is the physiological origin of most of ours): and they might experience the scene reflected in a decanter-stopper as a stroke of revelation. One might on this basis expect there to be, not insect neo-Platonists, but intrinsic animal preferences due to colour and form alone. Flowers are, in fact, information-carrying objects evolved in response to insect preferences, and subject, like the doyleys, to heavy sales-selection, for they depend on their customers to pollinate them. Now if animals show behavioural evidence of sensory preferences which do not depend on conditioning to, or instinctive pursuit of, something else, such as nectar, only human exclusiveness seems to stand in the way of calling this an aesthetic experience. At least it is difficult to distinguish it formally from an aesthetic experience. (Indeed, the only good reason for not applying the title 'aesthetic experience' to every sensation of wellbeing is that, like Freud's designation of what is sexual, it widens the term to make it conversationally useless. But I make the biological point here because I want to make it again later, in insisting that there is a connection between art and pleasure which goes beyond my own vulgar hedonism.)

We would still like to know whether the power to respond to 'beauty', and the aesthetic sense generally, are an evolved adaptation; if so, to what they adapted us, and, phylogenetically, when. Since not even the releasers which determine our response to feminine beauty—which take a very heavy selectionist responsibility—are fixed, there may not be much point in asking the question. The matter which appeals to us is wildly heterogeneous, and the thing most likely to be adaptive is the fact of responding to *some* stimulus in this way—in the fact of an 'aesthetic sense', not in its content. This is exactly analogous to the ethical sense of social animals. In pursuit of a universal content for it we are back with simple psychometric experiments on one hand and Jungian archetypes on the other. Human social inheritance, unlike bodily inheritance, is non-chromosomal, Lamarckian and cumulative. We have no other model in nature which is really comparable—birds, for example, differ from species to species in the relative amount of their behaviour which is imitated, innate, or imprinted—a halfway house between the two. The apparent aesthetic preferences of bower-birds show no free choice or judgment: they are compulsive—but at the same time we are coming to recognise that our own may be equally so. Whether there was ever a pre-human primate who bridged the gap between an 'aesthetic' appreciation of nature and an 'aesthetic' appreciation of objects he made himself cannot be shown—though this, of course, is the interest behind God's gift to the academic critic who dislikes modern painting—work on the pictorial interests of chimpanzees. Apes enjoy coloured messes, as we do—it would be more interesting to know if a chimpanzee who is conditioned to a reward when he sees a cube and a shock when he sees a sphere would try to model cubes, or avoid modelling spheres— whether, in fact, his art had any content.

A crudely experimental approach by scientists to such matters as form and imagery, or symmetry, is sometimes resented, but it is at least evident to most people that these are topics upon which experiment is possible. They are, in fact, subjects which really belong to psychology or to the study of techniques, and it is only incidentally that they became traditionally attached to criticism at a time when there was no experimental psychology so named. The evolutionary ideas I have been discussing do not belong to criticism either—they belong to evolutionary biology. Psychoanalysis is useful to a critic in understanding the motives and significance of a work, but it is not criticism—it is really a branch of human biology. Yet academic criticism must be a substantial activity. Whole university Departments live on it, especially in the United States—hundreds of graduates and thousands of amateurs subsist by metabolising literature. Pick up a dead writer and you start a scurrying as if you had turned over a dead bird—one Joyce or one Proust, let alone a Blake, can support a huge ecological microfauna, just as every scale of a coelacanth is good for a Ph.D. thesis. These people, like the burying beetles, must be doing something.

And indeed they are—some of the time they are guessing to fill the vacant spaces which belong ultimately to science but have not yet been reclaimed. Some of the time they are writing history, biography, linguistics or anecdote. Much of the time they are enjoying the satisfactions of controversy without having to run the risk of expressing opinions which matter. But the central and capital pretension of this type of criticism—and I do not use 'pretension' in a derogatory sense—is to make value judgments about works of art, and its assumption is that one can make such judgments.

Science has, as I have suggested, nothing to say about intellectual 'absolutes' (though it may have a great deal to say about values, if they are intelligibly defined). It has a certain amount to say about divergencies in taste which is important to criticism. Here I can use the word 'aesthetic' in a biological context to mean 'that which gives pleasure', or that which gives a specific sort of pleasure, without much risk of interruption. To see what colour or shape an owl or a chimpanzee found aesthetically agreeable we should see which of a number it chose. But this is only because dumb animals cannot publish books or teach at universities. For an artist to admit that he had no critical standard *beyond what pleases him,* or worse, what pleases others, would be a little disreputable (in any case he would be disbelieved): for a critic or a professor of literature to admit it would be felo-de-se.

For the majority of both occupations I think the admission would nevertheless be quite manifestly true. It would remain true in spite of the fact that many artists and professors have created large critical systems to justify their taste. There are obvious exceptions: people have produced and criticised art in terms of a standard which singlemindedly disregarded their real preferences, out of religious, political, or even scientific, zeal. But most of us would quite rightly reject their conclusions. There is a difficulty in aesthetic dogmatism which is absent from religion and politics. Aesthetics is by definition concerned at some point with likings, and the duty of liking that which we have convinced ourselves by argument that we ought to like is rarely discharged convincingly, even by zealots.

Medicine is currently acquiring from biology the idea of human polymorphism. This means that there may be not, as we once assumed, one kind of digestion which is 'normal', but a number of kinds, discontinuously distributed. If we want to restore a disordered digestion to 'normal' we must in this case first determine which normal. The people who tried to scrub the blackamoor were unaware of human polymorphism in colour—which is of two kinds, inherited and phenotypic; some men are Negroes, some men are white but sunburned, and some white men when sunburned are darker than others.

The significance of this in medicine and psychiatry is obvious, but contrary to appearances it has also a bearing on one of the pretensions—and functions—of aesthetic criticism. It is not very upsetting to criticism that a tone-deaf man cannot enjoy music, even if tone-deafness is heritable. Those of us who are not tone-deaf can condole with him and go on listening. But what about the suggestion that there is a true polymorphism in taste—not in the quality or the intensity of the taster's experience, but in appreciation of a given kind or school or manner in art?

We very well know there is, of course, and so does the critic: tastes differ. They differ in our society, but as a matter of fact it is rather unusual that they should. In tribal or very coherent societies, which represent most past human history, tastes do not differ, or differ over a remarkably restricted range, because they are the product of one tradition, of personalities which tend to be alike because society and upbringing have evened them—not as much alike as identical twins or inbred mice, but as alike perhaps as all the members of a breeding population of wild dogs: while in our society they are highly diverse—as different as the competitors in a large dog-show. Tastes in Balinese or Akan art differ internally very little by our standards—the range of tastes in our society, like the range of beliefs, personality-types and standards, is a true polymorphism—chiefly of the epigenetic or sunburned variety, but, no doubt, with some strictly genetic traits involved, like those which have been said to determine musical ability or a liability to schizoid thinking. Our society is a mixture, as it were, of the consequences of every upbringing from Samoan to Aztec. We have already seen how this diversity affects sexual behaviour—its effect on artistic behaviour is the same, and so to a large extent is the underlying mechanism. Thus tastes not only differ, they may differ irrevocably, and certain tastes correlate so closely with other personality traits as to be predictable. If all such people require cultural diet, but the diets palpably differ, then there must be more than one relevant standard of merit. This is good for me, that is good for the President of the Royal Academy. Pointless, then, if I like Matisse and he likes Munnings, for him to call me a poseur or for me to call him a 'square'.

The model of differing opinions in science or morals, which also have unconscious, and may even have physiological, determinants, is no help. We can deal with the idea that the moon is solid to me and hollow to you by an inspection of the facts. We can deal with the idea that burglary is right for the burglar and wrong for the burgled—the Existentialist argument, if I am not mistaken—because it is only in intellectual fiction that burglars burgle on principle. The common critical solution is to inject a moral tone into aesthetics and attempt to shame us into appreciation. But there is no duty to like Van Gogh or Beethoven, and no factual argument to be advanced. The most we can hope to generate by argument alone is understanding and respect for them. Liking is built in, though it can be greatly cultivated. The 'non-tasters' are missing something: we can say that a man who does not like Van Gogh or Beethoven is emotionally handicapped: and in spite of developing a perverse argument I know as well as you that some art is 'better'—more proficient, more original, able to produce deeper emotional responses, more intellectually interesting—than other. Merit of performance in art is evidentially arguable—but it would be very difficult for anyone influenced by the psychological sciences ever again to treat seriously the vast body of argumentative matter dealing with the respective *merits* of tastes, except when they bear on something which is not a matter of taste—the truth or falsity of contained ideas, for example.

Equally questionable is the spoken or unspoken preoccupation of formal criticism, almost since its invention, with the danger that the Inferior will Prevail—the fear, in short, of its fellow-men, which is very like, but even less justified than, the moralist's conviction that every generation is going to the dogs. Every generation is philistine and about to erect, in the pleasures it chooses, the tomb of all that the critic values—but the history of art does not read badly in retrospect. The most depressing passages in it have been due to the process of fossilisation which follows the conviction of guardianship, to which academies and censorships are monuments. A more recent monument is the prestige of Unpopularity in art of all kinds, which makes Criticism and Taste the defenders of—something—against the popular. This is not only an alibi for our work when nobody but our friends likes it: it is a magnification of the unpleasurable quite as perverse as the Puritan's, though its origins are different. There are critics in all the arts—poetry and music have some of the worst of them: painting is by comparison lucky—who pretend as conscientiously to enjoy the unpleasurable as the Puritan did to enjoy Sunday, and, far worse, to despise the pleasurable as superficial, and in each case the pretence eventually seems to convince the pretender.

When our fellow-men are depressingly wrong, it is not in getting pleasure where they do, for art which pleases has some merit in that fact, unless it is gammoning its audience at the same time. Far more usually they fail to get pleasure, either from something which is merely unfamiliar, and will please them later on, once it has become familiar (Wagner, Debussy, tubular furniture; Picasso's dual viewpoint at home for centuries in folk art, is coming to be at home in advertising; Dylan Thomas is getting a mass audience on records; Bartók, who 'once sounded like a conflagration, now sounds like a czardas'), or from something which is inherently difficult and requires, like higher mathematics or a foreign language, specific knowledge or aptitude to enjoy what it contains. Over the last two years a number of people amounting to a new audience have suddenly become able to enjoy the music of Schoenberg, not because he has become 'familiar', but because they have become used to listening to telemetering. This, if we think about it, is genuine appreciation—not like enjoying Scarlatti because he sounds like a barrel-organ: people who use telemetering have become occupationally used to listening to 'tone rows', and to detecting significant pattern in them. Accordingly they can enjoy similar pattern in music—they have acquired an aesthetic skill. This surely suggests what criticism should be about. It should be a dispassionate branch of advertising, analogous to consumer research. It should be out to lengthen the menu, not to campaign against the indigestible.

More and more I think that criticism and critics, as we now see them and have them, are best occupied in communicating not their dislikes but their enthusiasms. They are much more effective as guides and couriers than as custodians. I do not mean that there should be no adverse criticism—the reviling of gammon, incompetence and pomposity is a normal civic duty, which we partly delegate to critics and expect them to discharge with persistence and enjoyment. But it is very important, clearly, that they should distinguish these from mere difference, and recognise at what point they are dealing not with real vices but with a discrepancy between their own and their author's personalities.

This really means no more than that, in terms of the biological origins we gave to aesthetics, a critic ought to criticise the art he likes, and still more like the art he criticises. This is now quite exceptional. Several of the most eminent and vocal non-playing critics of poetry clearly do not like it, for they can stand it only when it is first rate. A man who likes women likes all women, unless they have quite intolerable vices, and even then he may like parts of them. There are obviously many writers—George Darley or Poe, for example—unbearable to these very weak stomachs, of whom someone who likes poetry will be bound to say 'how good!' or 'how bad!' alternately. It is the advantage of having poets rather than professors as critics that they can usually do this—Mr. Eliot is a case in point, for his appreciation is not limited to writers he admires. I have the impression that this Casanova approach is much commoner in painting than literature: the graphic arts seem to have been much less hard on a painter like Ingres, whose technique was vastly superior to his taste, than literary critics have been in judging a writer like Swinburne.

But what about standards of taste? What about the contents of the box on which Criticism has been sitting sentry all these years? Each generation of critics have given a different inventory of them. Most of the time that box has been empty, or nearly empty. We are left, and I frankly admit it, with the situation cultured men

have always feared, where taste is based on pleasure, and where a
work of art is good, or an experience beautiful, for critical
purposes, when the critic, or a decent proportion of the critic's
own culture, over a decent period of time, find it so. Previous
generations found Cowley inspiring and Donne quaint. They were
missing our experience of Donne. If we are broadminded with
them, as we would be with savages, we say that Cowley 'had
value' for them. What gave them pleasure in him gives us none.
In other words, we are missing Cowley. If our grandchildren
find Ella Wheeler Wilcox inspiring and Donne dull, we shall not
be there to argue the point, and there will be as learned Faculty
argument in defence of that position as any we use today. We
cannot put pressure on posterity by any known means. The
defence against nihilism here is not an absolute standard—(the
chief thing that aesthetics, like ethics, can learn from science and
the consequences of science is that abandonment of the absolute
for the empirical does not produce moral disaster)—but the fact
I stated earlier in a far less provocative context—that the human
aesthetic sense, like the human moral sense, is an adaptation
which generates another adaptation. Darwinism applies with
suitable modifications to art. I am suggesting that our criticism
should be Darwinian.

Most people who have looked both at art and at animals will
have noticed that there is a striking likeness between the diversity of any animal group—fish, shells, mammals—and the diversity of works of art. Each species of fish or shell in the British
Museum might easily be the work of a different artist developing
the given theme of 'fish' or 'shell', or of a different very talented
student given these as an exercise: each series of artistic treat-
ments of a theme might equally well be an evolutionary series.
The range of evolutionary variation in art styles—in the treatment of the figure, for example, or the writing of love poems—
shows many of the typical features of evolutionary variation in
animals: convergence, mimicry, extinction, fossilisation, sym-
biosis, specialisation, the filling of ecological niches. This is an
amusing analogy for the biologist in the art gallery or the artist in
the museum of natural history. But at the same time there is a
sense in which it is quite real. Literature or painting have this
appearance of similarity to a range of animals because they are the

product of a tangible form of natural selection, exactly as animal phylogenies are.

Poems and paintings, fish and molluscs, are all formed by certain environmental demands, and judged by their performance in use. A piece of work may easily be inflated by temporary factors, or overlooked by cultures or periods to which it is not adapted; rabbits have overrun Australia like the detective novel, while koalas are dying out, like epic poetry, except in artificial preserves. There operates on a long-term basis an effective natural selection of art which adapts it to Man, and it is this which settles the spread of a form or the extinction of a work. There are, as we all know, deplorable works of great durability, as there are improbable animals. If *Shandon Bells* or William Macgonigle produce pleasure in some subjects, and if aardvarks still survive, the persistence of all of these is evidence that even if we do not personally admire them they are plugging an ecological niche. *Charley's Aunt* survives because it is good theatre. Shakespeare survives for the same reason, and the difference is not mystical— simply that while one attempts less than the other, both succeed. If *Charley's Aunt* survives long enough for its diction to be archaic, future Arts Councils will produce it, and unborn Leavises, Richardses and Eliots analyse it. There is no artistic deficit that time and reputation will not heal. 'La poésie a ses monstres, comme la nature', and if they attain fossilhood their bones become venerable. The law, said Oliver Wendell Holmes, is what the Courts will actually do. Cowley has become dormant because we have no ecological niche for him. Donne has colonised conditions where he can spread. Art is that which people will actually read, listen to, look at. Accordingly, art which pleases nobody will not survive, however thickly it is encased in theory. It is as simple as that.

I can perfectly well understand the desire of the cultured critic to show himself fastidious and selective, and to make other people fastidious and selective: but I doubt very much if his activity has ever achieved this—whether, in fact, it has ever achieved anything. What we normally succeed in forming by laying down standards is not taste but fashion. In fifty years our tastes, our standards, our fastidiousness, and most criticism will have become tiresome and irrelevant to a degree, and interest our successors only as evidence of the state of mind with which the artists of the day had to contend—while the works we are judging are either full of their own unsupported vitality, often for reasons which would have shocked their authors, or as dead as nails. It is pointless to be depressed about the decline of public taste. A dinosaur would have been rightly depressed, as even Mr. T. S. Eliot has sometimes been, about the effect of natural selection on his traditional standards. He could not foresee that there would one day be animals which could dig up his bones and treat them with interest and respect, and if he had he would still no doubt have been sad that the standards of those animals would no longer be in the true reptilian tradition. They would stand a far better chance of being so if instead of being anxious about the future of his standards he had produced more variable offspring; and we can really only hope to direct the course of literary natural selection by giving it a bigger range of variation to select.

Really persistent dinosaurism in regard to the standards of posterity can be so smug that one is tempted, at the risk of reinforcing it, to treat it as astronomers sometimes treat the lay public, and make its flesh creep by predicting the future. Let me take a single example. A highly characteristic preoccupation of dinosaurs (quite distinct from the useful activity of encouraging people to express themselves intelligibly) is their mission to safeguard language against Debasement. This is a special case of the fear that the Inferior will Prevail. Now language is a direct product of natural selection. Nobody who writes in modern English can fail to value and respect it as a literary instrument. At the same time, it is bound, as we very well know, to change continuously and perhaps rapidly, both in sound and in meaning. When we use it in composition we are accordingly writing music which will be played, not on a temporally static fiddle, but on an actively growing tree. Much that we write will soon sound, in all probability, very different, if only because in fifty years it may be that the majority of those who speak it will be Asians and Africans with no tonic accent. We must reckon this change as a normal hazard of art—the sound of Elizabethan poetry has undergone almost as much change. Its significance must change likewise—a generation of English-speaking Asians who find Blake familiar and easy, and Keats unfamiliar and difficult, will like-wise attach new and (to us) outlandish meanings to words and to imagery. This too literature is built to survive. But in looking at the probable development of English in the still remoter future one needs, if one is a dinosaur, nerves almost as steady as in predicting the remoter future of the galaxy.

From boys' magazines most of us are vaguely aware of the brand of simplified English spoken by and to the inhabitants of New Guinea in their dealings with the European sailors and beachcombers of the last century. It is in essence lewd English divested of grammar and syntax and recast in the rough shape of the native languages. It is barely intelligible on paper—spoken, it is burlesque Basic English in which 'destroy' is *bagarimap*, and 'interpreter' is *tanimtok*.[71]

It is also a very typical instance of a seed dropped by a major language, which appears to have germinated. A sizeable com-munity now speaks nothing else, and the language is becoming 'creolised' (having reached the limit of initial simplification, that is, it has started to develop a characteristic and growing syntax). In time this will take it out of the stage in which it is heard as parodic English, and we shall hear it as a language in its own right. It will very shortly generate a literature.

Judging from the history of Latin, the progeny of 'our' litera-ture and literary language may easily be an ugly duckling like this. Granted, by the time it has developed it will not be English. But if English were incapable of change, if it were successfully embalmed by purists, this or another of its progeny would come to compete with it. Pidgin English is not suitable to convey, say, Blake's ideas or Eliot's ideas—at least, not yet. But these may not be the ideas our immediate successors want to convey. The growth of computer and translating-machine design, for which some form of pidgin English is highly suitable, might give such a language a surprising advantage. Dealing in ordinary English, the machine is said to have translated the Russian equivalent of 'out of sight, out of mind' into the two words 'invisible idiot'. Compared with a sensitive language which is hard to score accurately, 'suppose no can see, no more think of', or some such construction, has advantages. The chief of these is that it is a hard-centred language—the very paucity of words prevents it having overtones. Natural selection might very well be about to favour a language without overtones, not only for factual communication, but for the discussion of such important but ill-categorised ideas as rights, liberties and duties, so that for some animals to be more equal than others is immediately identifiable as what the Papuan language calls *tok gaman*. Some such change could easily become a condition of having political institutions compatible with our survival.

Clearly, if it does undergo this change language will not be decaying but developing in step with the demands made on it by man. By looking at the extreme case we can see that attempts to stabilise it by injections of critical preservative can have one effect only, the splitting or sloughing-off and eventual fossilisation of a dead literary language from the developing flesh. And the answer to dinosaurs who shake their bony heads over the sequestrum, saying that deterioration is evidently, then, unavoidable, and that there is no hope for the survival of the reptilian contribution to human culture, is that they are unduly depressed, and partly through arrogance. They might have more confidence in their progeny—their acquaintance with literary history and with the history of man should make them confident that if natural selection promotes a major change of this kind, what looks to a cultivated Jurassic taste like barbarous gibberish will expand, as soon as aesthetic and artistic demands are made on it, into another magnificent instrument for the human aesthetic sense to perform upon—embodying, in the process, most of the literary achievement of its source-language, as French, Italian and Spanish arose from equally barbarous residues of Latin and in due course generated the Renaissance.

When such changes occur in *language*, they are self-evident. My point is that the artist, whether obsessed with 'posterity' or not (he usually hopes, I think, that his work will last longer than he will), must expect equally radical if less obvious changes in *attitude*, which will make his future audience, if he has one, think as differently from his contemporaries as they speak or dress. If there were critical values *quod semper, quod ubique, quod ab omnibus,* this would be the process from which to extract them. On the analogy of evolution, a biologist might expect the chief of these to be adaptability. This is not an attribute of which literary or artistic critics make much—largely because most of them, even historians, are at heart quite insensitive to the size of the difference in attitude between past and present audiences; even after devoted scholarship they know, rather than understand, that the Homeric or Renaissance worlds were not quite like ours, but the awareness usually evaporates as the essay develops. In any case the principle-seeking critic is up against the same problem as the generalising biologist: we have for reference the works of art and the animals which are here—and they are here because they are here. We can, if we like, apply Pangloss' theorem, and argue that because an animal is here it must have been uniquely well-adapted, and because a structure persists in a selectionist world where everything is for the best it must have an advantage, which we will proceed to find. This meets the usual fate of objects which fly in ever-decreasing circles. In fact, in applying the 'judgment of posterity' to animals, we find that it tends to vindicate two distinct types—the unambitious but immensely durable, which have remained, like the brachiopod *Lingula* and the mollusc *Trigonia,* quite unchanged over recorded time; and the adaptable and technically uncommitted, like the mouse, which have changed without ever embarking on intense specialisation—without ever committing themselves to a unique and time-limited setting. These have not survived as individual forms but as traditions.

The evolutionary analogy applied to art breaks down at this point. Artistic fossils are alive, and nobody can tell when one or other of them, provided it can remain in physical existence, will come out of its shell and multiply. Time could send Shakespeare back into diapause and bring Cowley out. There *is* value in Cowley; it depends on our possessing the seventeenth-century point of view. But it remains true that art has its *Trigonias*—pottery patterns or figurines that pleased Minoans and still please us—and its adaptables, *Hamlet* or *Alcestis,* works which can stand being interpreted in a contrary sense from the maker's intention, by men who do not fully understand his language and imagery, share none of his attitudes or habits, and disagree with his opinions—and still take control of the situation. This is different from biological evolution and adaptation. Successive generations of reptiles developed overgrown scales as an adaptation to temperature control, and their descendants took advantage of these to fly—when the same process of adaptability appears in a work of art it is as if we were to see an *individual* lizard shed its teeth and tail in circumstances which favoured flight and a beak, and evolve before our eyes into a crow—without loss of personal identity.

A far better analogy, perhaps, is in the behaviour of viruses. These information-containing particles can lie dormant for long periods, they require living cells for multiplication, and they are highly specific. Once in susceptible cells, however, they can take over the host's information system and turn it to their own ends—incorporating parts of it, but making it think their particular chemical thoughts. It matters very little of what they themselves were originally a part—the vaccinia which protected me against smallpox was once part of a calf, who shared my background even less than did Homer. There are persons and cultures who are insusceptible to particular works. Sometimes this resistance is the result of immunity—there is a definite refractory period in any one culture after an attack of Swinburne or Landseer which appears to be of this kind. I cannot now have Flecker, because, like measles, I have had him before. Leaving aside the fact that all viruses which we recognise are noxious to their hosts, which is no part of the analogy, a critic of viruses, or a virus-making artist, will therefore take as his critical standards catholicity, high attack rate, and lack of immune response. We cannot be sure that true viruses arise spontaneously in animal cells, but if they do, the chemical information which was first marshalled in the cell of a mouse or an opossum at some remote period may still be imparting itself to mine, and compelling me to participate in the process. This is the posterity-conscious artist's object vis-à-vis 'posterity'. It may be quite incompatible with his short-term object—which is usually to express in terms of his own age and personality a set of experiences which are finely adjusted, vague, and wholly a product of one mind in one setting. In this case he will be wise to forget about posterity altogether. In due course, the work which he produces, shorn of all the qualities and subtleties which he thought important, arguing a case opposite to his opinions, and as comprehensible to its audience as a Donne sonnet would be to the pidgin-speaking Papuans, may still be generating positive entropy and controlling the chemistry of minds a thousand or more years from now, through its own inherent vigour.

It should be possible in theory to determine the nature of that vigour, and the seekers after aesthetic absolutes are welcome to attempt it. If they are willing to become scientists and do the thing properly they may well succeed—though in the process they will lose any wish to pursue 'absolutes' of the type which crypto-Platonist criticism has sought in the past. If they are not willing, and prefer to remain 'mere speculative intellectuals' without benefit of science, I strongly suspect that they will find in their hands only a purely mechanical irrelevance like the tune-playing doyleys.

VII

On Play and Earnest

Those that bring Devils upon the Stage can hardly believe in them anywhere else. To see Hell thus play'd with is a mighty Refreshment to a lewd Conscience and a byass'd Understanding.

JEREMY COLLIER: *A short View*, etc.

THE true profit of creative imagination—of art, in other words—is, as I have already suggested, very like that of erotic experience, which is its older twin—both may well be biologically patterned forms of play. There is a sense in which the problem of play activities in human society is the most important contemporary issue, and subsumes all the different matters about which I have been talking—the hard-soft antithesis in human thinking, the normality or otherwise of artistic activity, the peculiarities of human psychosexual development, the natural history of modern entertainments, the success of science in enabling us to control our surroundings and ourselves, and even the survival of Man.

Most mammals, and many lower animals, have a set of activities, simple or complicated, which they seem to enjoy, but which are not obviously related to their biological business in life. Some are simple satisfactions like the rolling of horses or the scratching of bears, which we share: an evolutionary ascetic can easily think of functions for rolling and for scratching, but both look at times as if they were undertaken for their own sake. Others are group activities, like the running play of colts and young animals generally, or the hydrobatics of porpoises, which look like corporate enjoyment of muscular and somaesthetic sensation, in plain French, *joie de vivre*. Yet others are mock activities—sham fighting—or rehearsal activities—the kitten hunting leaves—which combine this exploration of physical possibilities with instinctual development. One common feature of all these doings is that they discharge what are commonly described as tensions—the animal looks as if it enjoyed what it was doing and felt the better for it. It is arguable that most behaviour, like Freud's view of fantasy, is the result of some 'tension' or other which is gratified by discharge, as it is in eating or sneezing, and which becomes a discomfort if it is not dealt with, but there is about play a characteristic element of doing for the sake of doing which is its main distinguishing feature. Play is the chief occupation, besides eating and sleeping, of young animals, and the occasional occupation of older ones, where it tapers off into the real activities which kittens or colts simulate; but it persists in mating behaviour and between mates, and within the group of social animals, to the end of life—one can see a very old bull seal sham-fighting with babies which in a few years will fight him in earnest.

Whether animals engage in purely mental 'play', analogous to our humour or philosophy, cannot be ascertained without the ability to ask them. Ours may be of the muscle-flexing type, in the solving of needless problems for amusement, or of the type of the anticipatory substitute—the child's fantasy of being a king, an architect or a soldier. The highly characteristic thing about human behaviour in this respect is the ease with which it becomes *all* play. The adult lives of mammals and the activities they choose are rather rigidly patterned by instinct. Man's art patterned by education, society, conceptual thought and other factors, but all these have a strong tendency to become vehicles for the expression of aim-inhibited fantasies. In tribal societies these are at least corporate, and therefore no less functional than the bower-bird's pseudo-artistic behaviour. In societies like ours, where social pressure on the form of individual behaviour is negligible by the standards of past human experience, individual fantasy is the chief determinant of almost all that we do. The artist knows that when he writes fiction he does not write 'in earnest'. Modern Europeans and Americans do not in general live in earnest, or arrive at opinions in earnest, or even, under the influence of wars, traffic accidents and dietary habits, and the unconscious forces which they express, die in earnest. They are often at their most earnest—most 'purposively genuine'—over the more typically mammalian forms of play—physical competitive activity and mating display; or over the self-conscious fantasy which expresses itself in art.

The difference between hard- and soft-centred thinking is the difference between earnest and play. The difference between science and art is in its end-product the difference between earnest and pretence, though the scientist himself may well begin by playing at being a scientist, and may remain at the play level of motivation throughout in spite of the substantialness of his results. In neither of these cases is anyone endangered—they probably represent the universal human use of fantasy as motive. The use of monetary resources and other persons as adult toys is less commendable, and the really dangerous form of play-activity in our society is in the conduct of government and of public affairs. That is not in earnest either. We do not provide the children who discharge aggressive tensions in play with real firearms or real instruments of torture, though they seem with increasing frequency to get hold of them nowadays. We do not require our films and comics, which perform the same service for disturbed adults, to enact themselves in earnest, with real blood and real groans. The direction of our affairs by modern governments is no more in earnest—in carrying out rational objects by rational means, that is—than are the children who play at Redskins or the audiences who watch indestructible heroines maltreated. But its effects unfortunately are.

So in spite of our clearer perception of cause and effect, which in many ways sharpens the line between reality and pretence, the non-earnest or insightless society has typically less, not more, clear-cut play activities than primitive societies whose fantasies are corporate. It substitutes entertainment, which is not an activity, and even the bodily, muscle-flexing satisfactions of mammalian play tend to be experienced for choice at secondhand and as spectators—if we watch the audience at a football match, we shall find that they are playing at playing.

It is odd that our society, which makes an exorbitant use of movement of other kinds and for other purposes, has so little psychokinetic art. In English society, particularly, we spend a good deal of emotional energy in repressing gesture, but we seem to have no formalised outlet for the states of mind it would otherwise express. Psychokinetic 'release' may be represented by fidgeting, or by the rare occasons (chiefly sporting) when we lower the barriers against violent gesticulation; its most socially important biological manifestation appears now to be in motoring, itself not an activity, in the muscular sense—which can easily acquire the same expressive quality as a primitive dance, but is a highly dangerous vehicle for the expression of moods.

The need for an expressive form of movement, and the fact that we feel deprived without it, can be seen from the speed with which even a superficially unpromising activity like student folk-dancing acquires content. Even with inexpert performers a foursome reel between two mutually-jealous couples looks quite different from the same figure danced by a pursuer, a pursued, and two lovers—which is as it should be. Dancing, at least in our society, is a form of play, but one of which we make oddly little psychological use. Ballroom dancing maintains itself in equilibrium between the public, which shows signs of wanting perpetually to use it as an expressive medium, and the teachers of dancing, who, for obvious reasons, prefer a standardised skill and are against improvisation. So long as its chief use, apart from being an adult game of skill, is erotic, the public is bound to retain a small start. This is reflected in the history of the popular dance: the waltz and its congeners originally swept the field because they gave a socially-permitted opportunity for body contact between the sexes. Now that we can have this without stylised pretexts, we seem to be turning to the 'open' dances of Latin-American origin which can be, and are, expressive and abreactive; rock 'n' roll is a possible alternative to postural backache in a way that the waltz is not. Nordau was quite right in saying that the dance has shrunk—not only from its vast social importance in tribal cultures, but even from its recreative importance not so long ago. We have no currently popular dance which can really be used to interpret anything except courtship—partly because we have so few *activities* (hunting, fighting and the like having gone), and only sailors have expressed their work in dances within living memory; and partly because the protagonist dance, like most other expressive modes, is now professional—(in its prestige form as ballet it is interesting in being the one art with a mass following at which the members of the audience can make absolutely no showing: an amateur violinist can at least play the notes, or some of them, which he hears the virtuoso play and consequently he has more than a collector's interest in their technique). The protagonist dance is far more at home under conditions where the dancers are expected by the spectators to express their moods better, but not so very much better, than they can themselves. It was part of Fred Astaire's genius that he always introduced into his virtuoso act steps which his audience could dance with their girl friend. Neither ballet, nor scaled-down forms of it such as eurhythmics, now fit into this pattern: nobody can join in the first, and I doubt if anyone wants to join in the second. When a protagonist dance does take light, as it should in a society which knows how to play, and a film sets a cinema-full of youngsters dancing, we send for the police to restore the traditional absence of expressive gesture.

There is only one formal artistic activity to which we apply the word 'play', and here the word is used frankly as an antithesis to what is said or done in earnest. Dancing and drama come equally naturally to man, but the use of the second is repressed on the way to adulthood before the use of the first, by the need to distinguish 'let's pretend' from false pretences—pretence, as we saw in considering the hard- and soft-centred modes of thought, is strong stuff owing to the vividness of the human imagination and the strength of the human wish-power; the border between acting and doing, real and imaginary, is too easily blurred. If the elaboration of dancing has been lost because we have lost the intense sense of corporate movement, the common body-image, which simpler societies have had, the restriction of drama to set contexts where there is no risk of confusing real and imaginary seems to reflect the ethnic process of growing-up into hard-centredness which has given us science. The drama we have retained has lost, at least at the conscious level, several of the motives which were still present in Greek, and are always present in primitive, play-acting—the importance of taking the name and identity of someone else, the enacting of something as a fully effective substitute for the reality, and likely to bring it about—

and the idea of 'being', or being possessed by, a god or person. None of these would seem at first sight to be represented in the modern commercial drama—though, as we shall see, having been ejected by hard-centredness they have got in again by the rear entrance.

The most interesting part of the natural history of drama in our own society is probably not so much the play and its motives, as the origin and motives of the desire to act. Primitive plays are performed, like dances, quite as much for their effects on the actors as on any non-participant who happens to be there: where they are ceremonial there may be no audience—in fact they may be strictly secret. At a slightly later stage the actors are mysta-gogues and the audience initiates: in the present, final, stage, the actors are illusionists and the audience peasants. So long as the stage has its present exorbitant publicity value and prestige, there will be no lack of people who wish they were on it, but the special cathexis of drama for the actor is something of which it would be interesting to know more—in particular, about the effect of acting on the actor's sense of personal identity, and whether the stage selects people who wish to act out particular scenes or to assume other identities.

It is with author and audience rather than the actor that I am concerned here, however. We have currently two kinds of enter-tainment which involve acting. One is commissioned, as it were, by the audience, or a section of it—the other by the author. These correspond to the division with which we should by now be familiar as characteristic of modern literature, between comic-book art and prestige art: and as in other instances the two are more alike than they appear at first sight to be.

The art of the commercial film is, without much dispute, the comic-book *plus,* the realisation of censored erotic fantasy by way of a set of situational fetishes, which is now the preferred enter-tainment of a very large section of the civilised world from child-hood on. The film and television version of this is historically new, in that the fantasy can be presented on a more impressively realistic scale than ever before. In fact, it can be confused with reality: on coming out of the worst films there is a noticeable change of gear to the pattern of everyday life which we seldom experience in reading. The closest analogues of such dramatics are probably the little plays presented in the course of the Roman games, which fitted the real execution of some obnoxious person into a suitable charade, or the *scènes speciales* enacted in Jean Genêt's brothels. All that is missing to equate them with the second is the opportunity for the clients to participate—I would not be surprised if a commercial *genre* of this kind eventually sprang up: at present the audience has to be content with identification—though it can already buy records of one-sided dialogue enabling it to 'play opposite its favourite screen personality'.

Before we contrast this matter too contemptuously with the prestige plays which we, as intellectuals, patronise, write, or permit ourselves to enjoy, we should recognise the relationship between the two: in the prestige play the author is commissioning the fantasy to suit himself instead of a box-office—how much he puts into it besides the events which, like Flaubert, he 'wishes to see', will depend on his general ability: *Salammbô* and *Madame Bovary*—are they not the two perfect X certificate films, one popular, the other intellectual?

We come back accordingly to the same point regarding drama as with the other literary forms—in our society it is a vehicle for individual acting-out. The novelist does this in his head and without help. The dramatist needs co-operation to bring the fantasy-presentation into real presence, or its semblance. His instructions control the behaviour of a group of volunteers in the fantasy situation so that it will be what he wishes, not what comes naturally to them. The dramatist's relation to his actors is in this very like the neurotic's would-be relation to other people, but for him the cast will co-operate, because pretence is their occupation, while for poor Emma they would not. The neurotic is casting for a plot which, unlike the author, he does not usually divulge to others—the commonest outcome of a marriage between neurotics is a trial of strength between actor-managers, each attempting to dictate the other's lines, and each refractory to being 'produced'.

One might have expected this analogy, which is probably often conscious so far as the playwright is concerned, to have conferred a particular insight of the drama in its dealing with interpersonal relations—an insight comparable to that shown by the endless plays which have taken advantage of the theme of tolerated pretence to discuss the difference between real and imaginary, acting and being, self and persona, in terms taken from the theatre. This is a recurrent theme which is natural to the set drama. One would expect the complementary theme—the neurotic as actor and would-be producer among people who are not acting, or not acting his particular play, to have found its Pirandello.[73]

And, indeed, by far the most popular modern topic of the Anglo-American prestige play, is the presentation of neurotic behaviour. Our culture has an appetite for watching this second only to its appetite for violence. But in spite of an enormous amount of 'psychology' this behaviour is not there to be analysed, nor is it presented realistically. It is there to be manipulated, and the intention behind the treatment is Emma Bovary's intention, to insist that the world is as I wish it. The magical intention of the primitive 'play' is back. This tradition of drama slips as expertly from under the demands of insight as the comic-book sets aside probability, by transferring the neurotic intention to the characters—we watch them raving and muddling themselves on the author's behalf, and derive an illusion of insight from it, but in fact they are acting out his chosen unrealities quite as unashamedly as are the cowboys and the kidnapped, indestructible girls of the simpler tradition. This is what happened to Flaubert, once more, but without the incidental insight which his choice of the Delamare-Bovary story gave him in realising it. The horse operas give us our psychosymbolic wishes upon one hand—the O'Neills and Tennessee Williamses minister to our self-pity, as well as our social and political inactivity, on the other.

The great original of this modern tradition of psychological drama is Ibsen. There is a curious similarity to W. S. Gilbert in the number of Ibsen plays which have a stock cast—as Blake has his comic shadow in Sterne, the harlequinade has its prestigious shadow in Ibsen, and most of the figures of the subsequent development of this tradition are already present in him. There is the father-figure who is in disgrace, or about to be so—there is the Nogood Boyo figure; the Iago figure who finds out and tells about the hidden shame; the Dionysus-figure (a scruffy academic who may blend with one of the other characters or appear on his own), and above all the catalyst, the Woman, good or evil, who has the innate capacity to set unattended boulders rolling by accident or design: there are the symbols which are emblematic rather than symbolic—the white house, the snowstorm, the indoor forest, the Destroyed Great Work or the Unborn Child. As with Dickens, we can recognise the marionettes as the fauna of Ibsen's own exasperated background—his father's bankruptcy, the galling ostracism of the righteous neighbours, the girl whom Ibsen never forgave for making him fall in love with her, the illegitimate child born when he was eighteen, whom he 'buried' by refusing ever to see him, the search for recognition among the stiff-rumped, stinking bourgeoisie whom he so hated and so wished to join—there is the super-bourgeois that he eventually became. At this level the plays are brilliant—as maps of the author's experience. The characters are departments of himself. Unlike Dickens, however, he never opens the windows, let alone the door, to admit live figures from the street.

In greeting Ibsen as a new influence in the theatre, Shaw went out of his way to point to the artificiality of motive in Shakespeare—Iago is there, not because he is likely, but to catalyse a tragedy: Romeo and Juliet die of bad luck, not inevitability. He decries the stock situations of the 'social' play, represented by Pinero and his imitators: Ibsen had been sent to change all that. Yet in fact, though Shaw did not see it, Ibsen's work follows a formula as mechanical as Pinero's, differing from it only in that Pinero's convention is based on obsessions which are social, while Ibsen's obsessions are personal. Each, like Emma Bovary, is grossly falsifying reality.

The figures in Ibsen are acting-out—they are behaving as it gratifies the author to see them behave. There is no observation of real-life psychology behind them. They respond to stock Ibsenian situations with stock Ibsenian gestures; not as real neurotics act, but as they fantasy themselves acting: these gestures are neurotic, and there are no foils to them—nobody ever acts reasonably, takes coherent measures against a threatening situation, or misses an opportunity to gratify their emotions. These are the ancestors of the fauna of emotion-seeking, imaginary problem adults who have infested the stage ever since in the plays of O'Neill or Tennessee Williams—people who never work, except at symbolic treatises or tasks which they despise, who never think when they can feel, who have no sense of the ridiculous, who never ask advice. Even in an age of real neurotics, for whom one can feel sympathy, they are unreal—less real in Ibsen than in his successors. 'People don't do such things!' says Tesman, when Hedda shoots herself—and truth breaks in. People don't, or rather, they don't for these conventionally emotive reasons. Flaubert, who knew his neurotics intimately, has no such illusions. Emma Bovary kills herself out of fright, spite and lack of cash. Ibsen would make her do it on principle—Flaubert is nearer the mark in letting her *pretend* that she thinks she is doing it on principle. Nobody else shares the fiction. When Rosmer and Rebecca set off to drown *à deux*, like exhibitionistic teenagers, how one wishes they would jump and find the stream frozen solid! If Chekhov had invented them, it *would* have been.

I am not being hard on Ibsen for expressing his own emotional conflicts. He made them into powerful works of art; how powerful we can see by comparing them with Strindberg, where the balance tilts into sheer complaint. The acid note in what I have said about him comes from exasperation, not at his problems, but at his influence, and this is unfair. His insight is not consistently bad—it ebbs and flows. In *The Lady from the Sea* he shows the resolution of a neurotic conflict in genuinely insightful terms: in *A Doll's House* someone acts resolutely to break the chain of sentimental falsehood: in *An Enemy of the People*, finally, we see Ibsen as he must often have wished he could be, aggression fully turned outwards—revenging himself on the Gadarene swine unhampered by grandiose emotions, in a manner which is at least vigorous. Of these three plays the first two at least end not in neurotic gestures but in resolution of one or another kind, and in the third the fantasy is a stout-hearted one. In *The Lady from the Sea*, Hilda teasing the dying man is the Medusa-figure, who appears full-grown in Hedda and Rebecca, at an early, tadpole stage, and here her behaviour springs explicitly 'from the lack of a kind word from her stepmother'. In the play which comes closest to real personal insight, then, Ibsen clearly got at the origins of his boulder-rolling man-destroying Medusa and exorcised even her.

Ibsen, like Shelley, clearly fought for self-knowledge and won it, if only in part. Unfortunately it is not the influence of this courageous progress which has persisted. Others lack his stamina. He is rather the parent of the shouting, gesticulating, exhausting sensitives who invade the theatre, and more recently invade our homes, in the modern prestige play. They and their troubles do not purge our emotions, so much as make them itch, and make us scratch them. Anti-conventional as they were, Ibsen's plays did much to set a convention, not of drama only, but even of behaviour, or at least of response to emotional blows in social contexts, as extravagant as that of Greek tragedy, without the excuse of Até and the Gods, the tradition of self-dramatisation made respectable. Ibsen transferred the emotive material of the melodrama to an intellectual level and made it persist unrecognised as the chief modern manner in serious theatre. It is intellectual— pretentiously so in the more modern progeny of the tradition— but there is never any sign among the characters of intellect at work—thinkers and professors are shown with prestigious awe, but they are never shown thinking. At the same time, all manner of emotional demonstrations—suicide in particular—are given intellectual motives and intellectual prestige. The usual motives of such actions in real life are not Nietzschian metaphysics but disorders, either of mood or of character.

There is a striking similarity between what has happened here to the theatre, and what we saw happening in the novel, as it undergoes division into hokum on one hand and actuality on the other. A Tennessee Williams play is psychological drama only in the sense in which the comics are psychological literature. One could suggest several reasons why the apologetic dramatisation of character defects should have made such headway in English and American, and so much less in French, drama. I suspect that one possible reason is our prestige rejection of comedy in favour of the contrived Unhappy Ending, which is a residue of Puritanism, but it might equally be the other way round: the capacity to write comedy implies insight into our own failings as well as those of others—the celebration of the unbalanced in drama has as its object the satisfaction which used to be called Byronic, and a sense of comedy punctures them as effectively as Pushkin's *Eugene Onegin* punctures the character of the would-be Manfred. Pushkin is not the only Russian who does this—I have already suggested what Chekhov would have done to Ibsen's characters. The ability to put the soulfully self-occupied in their place, or out of their misery, is a recurrent aptitude in Russian literature, and a highly-valued one, because of the unusual frequency with which such people seem to occur there. The shallow emphasis on the 'positive' in modern Russian fiction may not only be the result of political censorship—it may also reflect final exasperation with a long tradition of narcissistic, endlessly talking sensitives; selfish, ineffectual and waiting to seize on any practical emergency for a theatrical display—it may represent, in fact, the revolt of the Junos against an intelligentsia of Paycocks, Karamazovs and Emma Bovarys for whom emotion is a cheaper form of vodka, and who can be relied upon, when the roof is on fire, to discover something for which they have to atone. I see something of this exasperation in the attack, indefensible as it was by our standards, on Pasternak—it is in part the reaction of a literature and a people which has had to defend itself not only against tyrants, famine and cold, but simultaneously against grandiloquent suicides and doctors who spend their time, when surrounded by the casualties of war and hunger, feeling their own pulses.

Invalids who are too voluble eventually lose our sympathy, try as we may. We run the risk of a similar reaction among publics, and above all among theatrical audiences, to the cult of person-ality-disorder in theatre. It is probably more in evidence there than in the novel, because the rows and speeches, the quarrels and gestures of the immature and the unbalanced attract our atten-tion—they have always been good theatre, indeed, in real life we call them theatrical, as we speak of making a scene. The pseudo-psychological tradition replaces a series of others, in all of which some pretext had to be found for the presentation of noisy, demonstrative or at least intense emotion—the mixed-up intellectual replaces the dedicated villain of melodrama and the fate-haunted hero of post-Classical tragedy. If we displaced our worse moods and our more irrational moments from drama there would be little left, and I do not suggest that we will or should—but we might well cease to treat them as the badge of the intellectual way of life, for no other theatrical tradition does so, and ours has not done so for long. The blistering row between the General and his wife in Anouilh's *Waltz of the Toreadors*, which drags out into words the unspoken hostilities of every marriage there ever was, hostilities which marriage depends upon keeping silent: or Shakespeare's clinical picture of Richard the Second, spiteful, unbalanced, conceited and ceaselessly rhapsodising—but nevertheless a fellow human being; they are not 'positive', in all conscience, but the treatment of them is. Shakespeare, indeed, probably had quite a different intention, and wanted us to share Richard's estimate of himself as kingly and even Christ-like in his resignation, but, as with Shylock, who began as a stereotype to be hated, the reality of the observation takes charge.

The short answer is that our psychological drama has lost most of its social relevance by becoming sentimental instead of psychological, so that like the Victorian melodrama which it replaces we do not experience or evaluate it—we can only take a bath in it, as the author has done, or stay away.

There is, moreover, another very similar type of theatrical representation in progress, in which a fantasy is likewise enacted by those who do not share it, and from which we may have more difficulty in 'staying away'. The process we know as government, which now determines national policies, has always been composed of two halves—a side which has some practical bearing on real events and purposes, and a side concerned solely with self-dramatisation for some or all of the power-holders. This is in no sense a new problem. But the balance between the sides has changed rapidly in the last few years with the development of complex scientific cultures. In this generation, much which has always been a matter of soft-centred intuition and opinion has become open to operational methods. Decisions in all fields of practical action are now taken in this way—and consequently in earnest. The exceptions are the few, key, directional decisions, between guns and butter, between purpose and nonsense. The vast budgets and the casts of thousands, backed by admirable technology, which Hollywood used to pour into the creation of its comic-book epics, are now models of the pattern in our public life. We have a society which is effectively decapitated: it has enormous resources, brilliantly maintained—they are directed and allocated, not to 'achieve the possible', but by experts in the art of *preventing* the possible so that they can divert these resources into the enactment of fantasy—into what is, for all the purposive value there is in it, play-therapy for themselves. These dramatists in public affairs, like their stage counterparts, require the co-operation of a cast. The dramatists of the neurotic school reinforce their defence mechanisms by making other individuals act out their fantasies, but the play is play, the cast are paid professionals, and when it is over they will go home. Strindberg and O'Neill had no powers of conscription. There is the difference.

The effects of parliamentary democracy have been in many ways unexpected. Since it now appoints leaders by public theatrical competition, using the methods of the entertainment industry, it tends to act as a personality sieve which promotes selectively people with an ingrained wish to use public affairs in this manner. Under these conditions the first—and, as we see it in the modern English and American parties, virtually the only—object of policy is to stay in office; those who might have ideas beyond self-dramatisation are obliged to concentrate on this, and on policies which can be promoted by Barnum and Bailey methods: with the result that while Marxist governments, in spite of a deal of psychopathology, are at least directional in their decisions (their play is full of cathectic situations, but it has a plot) no Western government has any policies, other than military ones which extend beyond the next general election: and, finally, since most administrative and organisational decisions now require knowledge, government as conducted by Cabinets is becoming drained of all practical relevance, and, indeed, of all content apart from the enactment of psychodrama.

The impact of this now falls on all of us, but the scientist is in one sense the person most heavily affected. Through the application of science the expectation of life in most Western countries has risen over the last two centuries from about thirty years at birth to about seventy. A child, even an underprivileged child, in Holland or Britain or New Zealand can therefore now expect to grow up, to avoid fatal disease in early adulthood, to produce children who will grow up, and to reach middle age. He can reasonably expect to do this without ever having been exposed to plague, cholera, typhus or smallpox; without ever having lost a wife in childbed or a child in infancy; and without ever having experienced the annihilating physical work which the child Nekrassov saw, when the resting *bourlaki* told him that they wished they could die.

All these developments rest on existing knowledge and techniques. In the next ten years they could be made available to the majority of human beings, for the first time in the history of the species. If things go on as they are, we know that they will not be made available. Let us limit it still more. It would be possible beyond any doubt, I think, to guarantee that at the end of the decade there will be no more untreated cases of leprosy, malaria or yaws in the Commonwealth. This is a modest objective. It presents no unusual scientific or practical difficulties—it could be set in motion beginning tomorrow. And it will certainly not be, as things now stand.

Why not? Not for lack of resources, not for lack of theoretical information—not because of practical drawbacks in the field. If it could in some devious way be made into a destructive, a military, or a fantasy-fulfilling project—if we could conspire to convince the policy-makers that these diseases were not natural, but put there by the Russians—it would be done, not in ten years but in two. We know this—in fact, when public health workers discuss the chance of putting the social possibilities of science into effect, they no longer ask whom the project can be made to pay, but whom it will be necessary to frighten—how it can be written into the comic-book, so that a serious project can be disguised in a form sufficiently pathological to pass muster as play.

The Swiss criminologist Reiwald[73] draws a distinction between satisfactory and unsatisfactory forms of crime. Rape, murder, violence and sexual aberrations are satisfactory forms of crime. They are the matter of 'strong' literature, of modern entertainment, and of pathological fantasy. Smuggling, swindling, driving when drunk, are unsatisfactory crimes. They do not produce the same glow, either of curiosity or righteousness, and nobody clamours, red-faced, for equally pathological penalties to be visited on them. Our culture is now drawing exactly the same distinction, between satisfactory and unsatisfactory activity, satisfactory and unsatisfactory science, in its priorities—and in what, as against its pretensions, it is actually doing. The choice bears no relation to purpose or to reality. Nuclear weapons are the supremely satisfactory ingredient for the comic-book plot —abolition of yaws, provision of protein in African diets, are unsatisfactory, and that, so far as priorities are concerned, is that.

Satisfactory to whom? In one sense, no doubt, to all of us, as hokum in novels and the theatre is satisfactory to all of us. In Freudian terms, the factors which make crimes, fantasies, situational fetishes and the scientific projects selected by governments 'satisfactory' are identical and near-universal. But it is patently false to suggest that we are all to blame, or that this pathological system of priorities in real life has been created by popular demand and simply embodies original sin. We read comic books and murder reports: we may be excited by them—but we do not usually act them out; nor did we employ Jack the Ripper to act on our behalf. We are aware to this extent of the gap between play and earnest—not always, not perfectly, but better than that. Patently neurotic considerations are steering our civilisation in all its most important decisions, but the choice of policies is not the democratic expression of public fantasies, in spite of assiduous propaganda to make it appear so. The public was not the prime mover in insisting that all our energies should go into them. It was not even told when most of the decisions were made— they reflect the determination of a very small group of individuals who have set themselves, like authors, to enlist the whole society in their game of acting-out, individuals who are where they are, doing what they are doing, precisely because their sense of the distinction between real purpose and personal fantasy in public affairs is blurred. To do this they must occupationally prevent the possible, turn the world into a play of the neurotic school, and take elaborate measures to ensure that we do not anticipate or alter their choices in the interests of some real, adult emotionally 'unsatisfactory' purpose.

The 'satisfactory' world which is envisaged by the art of preventing the possible is both familiar and unattractive. It is now no longer the world of Mr. Tennessee Williams—even distorted human emotions are quite absent from it: it belongs to the cartoon. In fact there is no reference in it to the business of everyday life at all; nor is there any more plot than in those tedious serials, produced for a select audience, which deal exclusively with flagellation or leather boots. Instead, we have a peculiar mental territory, studded with Freudian but otherwise useless projectiles and the enormously costly equivalent of tin soldiers, pitted with satisfactory crises, blistered with satisfactory summits at which new alcoholics can bawl abuse at fresh senile dements who have double-crossed them, traversed by negligible V.I.P.s in the tunic of Superman, and enlivened by the perpetual and deeply satisfactory shadow of world annihilation under which little men, like adolescents with flick knives, look and feel big. In doing so, not only do they prevent the possible, they undo what has been done. They may do so finally, for they provide equipment with which real and dangerous psychotics, which most of them are not, or even accident, may easily translate satisfactory fantasy into real genocide and real suicide at our expense. This is an even more dangerous situation than the unregenerate capitalist condition in which the possible was contingent on private acquisitiveness—profit at least is a reality-centred notion, and though it might not infrequently lead to murder it did not usually lead to intentional suicide. None of the present mythology of priorities in our civilisation, thus directed and stage-managed, is related to reality at all. Cardboard missiles would serve the same purposes more cheaply, without running our present risks. Instead, we have the truly astounding sight of the bulk of the technical and intellectual efforts of man being diverted down the drain of a few individuals' imaginations —producing incidentally to this, and out of what is little more than the salvage and offcuts, a transformation of life for the better striking enough to show what could be done with the whole—pyramid-building, but in a form which actively endangers human survival, as well as blocking advance.

The extreme comic-book manifestation of this process is at present almost uniquely Anglo-American. In the Communist countries it has taken a form which is more traditional, the demand for intellectual conformity. Most of the application of science in Western countries has taken place in spite of the power-holders, who have only just begun to realise its dramatic possibilities as an adjunct to their play. Communist power-holders have used science for real purposes on a remarkable scale, but they have tried to tamper intermittently with its content, while ours leave it free in mind but attempt to enlist it for pathological projects. Our version is now the more physically dangerous, but theirs began to affect the validity of science for any purpose, and it may prove eventually that it is in the Marxist world, rather than here, that the initial battle has begun to be fought consciously between the requirements of real purpose in science and of pathological fantasy in the direction of human affairs.

This conflict of the purposes of living with irrational authority is manifestly the most important issue for this generation, and the existence of democracy may have delayed our appreciation of it by making us confuse irrationality with open tyranny. In spite of differences, the problem is now becoming essentially the same in all cultures: how are we to control the psychopathology of otherwise normal people in office? If we want to live in earnest, not the fantasy of the deranged—if, in fact, we want to live at all, we must do so. In politics we are now never far from the nursery. I remember being convinced by a Marxist-minded colleague that Freud's interpretation of behaviour was really too simple to be politically relevant—and opening the paper to read that a certain meticulous defender of stubbornness and the acquisitive society, who spent his life thwarting diabolical enemies, accumulating alliances, hanging on, in the attempt to get his own way, up to and past the brink; working with single-minded devotion towards a final revenge on Them which would take the form of a vast, dirt-scattering explosion—had died at last, *of bowel disease!*

One possibility—that which people in earnest have often used in recent years to harness the existing system, and divert part of our resources back from play to reality—has been to incorporate some constructive project into the story, as it were, of the comic strip. Suppose that a conspiracy of unusually public-spirited scientists were to study all the accidental deaths in the world— famine, traffic and disease included—and by an effort of secret international co-operation they were to fabricate evidence that these accidents were in reality the work of a malicious Adversary —say the Martians: the Devil is too long dead to serve. Suppose that they successfully kidded and frightened their governments— exactly as they now have to do, when a constructive project has to be got through. They would find that the protein deficiency of Africa was part of an organised strategy of conquest; and protein deficiency in Africa would be relieved, if it meant despoiling

Europe, emptying the sea, and conscripting babies in arms—the chief problem would be to keep the overreaction of the Napoleons at the top, who now view the matter with complete apathy, within reasonable bounds. We would see the American, Russian and British Summits bawling allied defiance at Mars, as they did at Hitler, and their respective scientists and publics co-operating with their tongues in their cheeks and a song in their hearts. Malaria, road accidents, hookworm, leprosy, all of them would be put down in rotation to the Enemy, and projects would be authorised in order to remove them. Finally, with luck and ingenuity, we would set the Wild Hunt on psychopathology and irrational dominance behaviour in office, isolate and, if possible, set the decision-takers to remove themselves—after which the survivors could safely be told the truth. We would have got our hands on the plot and produced them out of existence, though it might be necessary, *faute de mieux*, to do so by exciting their Ibsenian impulse to run violently down a steep place into the sea and be choked.

So far from being a wholly frivolous suggestion, this is in fact almost the usual method now by which technicians and civil servants secure support for useful work—they exploit the fear, conceit and jealousy of the decision-takers so that their castration anxieties produce rockets for space research and their heart attacks money for fundamental research in medicine. No doubt our Russian colleagues use a fluent acquaintance with Marxism in the same way. Something very like it has happened in the history of revolutionary science, and of science in wartime, but these in themselves suggest why it will not do. We cannot effectively build the future out of chips from a pyramid. So long as psychopathic policies are there at the root of the decision-taking process, we shall find outselves baulked in exactly the way that Soviet, or our own wartime, science was sometimes baulked by the emergence of political fantasy-making to divert it from the fruits of its purposive activities. Not only is the problem becoming identical in the two chief competing cultures, but there is ultimately only one solution, which is the same in each case—the growth of active resistance among the generality of individuals to inclusion in the cast of the fantasy-production, to the production itself, and to the producers. This is particularly true of scientists and technicians, the supposed apostles of the purposive against the non-purposive mode—for them the traditional ways of justifying a sitting posture, in terms of neutrality, the carrying out of *soi-disant* democratic decisions, or plain ear-shutting will no longer do. Apart from anything else, they face the germ of new Lysenko situations, in both the East and the West, which threaten the content of science itself. The reason that, as the public cynically recognises, official scientists invariably support official fantasies on scientific grounds is not that they have been bribed or threatened, but that governments are becoming expert in selecting experts who will participate in their fantasy. They are casting their piece with greater skill. We are now encountering instances in the West where a pathological scientific tail—ready to fabricate experimental results and publish the fabrications—is wagging a reluctant political dog; into the continuance of nuclear tests, for example.

I have drawn together the manifestations of play and earnest in our society, and in doing so I have introduced an issue so much more significant than those of literary criticism that it makes the discussion of books look irrelevant. I can fully sympathise with anyone who thinks that we waste our time writing when we should be fighting. Other people will probably be disappointed that in these papers I have not set out to carry a torch for the critical and spiritual value of creative imagination as Blake saw it: they see in it, as he did, the missing factor in contemporary life which accounts for their sense of deprivation among potential plenty. The deprivation is real enough, but it is more complicated than that—its chief origin is in the loss of our sense of sociality, a loss which predates Blake, and of which he was well enough aware. This in turn has had a variety of causes, but its remedy is in applying to our own social and mental processes the operational methods which we have applied to disease, which will give us the knowledge, and in cultivating our desire for life and the emotional products of life, which will give us the motivation, to deal radically with our chief social problems, the abuse of power. In so far as art can do the second it is an ally, but it must not hinder the first, nor act as a local or a general anaesthetic

155

against evils in society or against our responsibility to our neighbours.

It may be asked why I have more confidence in sex than in art not to make us self-preoccupied. Mystical and near-mystical satisfactions, to which the 'creative imagination' is prone, have a drawback which frankly erotic enjoyment has not, that they tend to damp down our belligerency in defence of our own, and other people's, social rights, while adult sexual satisfactions, and the social relationships they generate, have a way of heightening it. In particular, they are peculiarly able to make the unconscious mechanism of identification which confuses Little Father and Big Brother with our own natural parents, and underlies much of our political supineness, boomerang against those who now exploit it for their own ends. The last thing a dictator should say —as Shelley could have told him—is 'Let me be your father'.

Our success in coming alive out of this century is going to depend less on our own individual adjustments viewed *en masse* than on our ability to show enough unorganised belligerency to control a rather small and relatively deranged body of individuals who now direct our affairs. The cultivation of science can make us aware of unreason. The cultivation of love gives us wives, mistresses, children, family life, and makes us aware of pleasure, all of which are threatened by policies which prefer the satisfactions of hate, war, espionage, nuclear destruction and personal aggrandisement. In these two matters we are in earnest. Both consequently make us fight back. The inward-looking creative imagination may not, though it should, and at the moment often does not (artists are perpetually encouraged to use their art as an alibi for not being out on the barricades at critical moments for human survival). Nor, unlike science, does it help us to attain control over the mental processes involved, unless we are clear, at the outset of the imaginative process, what we are about. We can set out to 'experience' our mind or to understand it. The second does not preclude the first, but uncontrolled enthusiasm over the results and importance of the first may hinder the second. Understanding is a long business barely begun—what we have understood withdraws nothing from the creative experience, which will always be worthwhile *for itself,* as art is 'more' than a congeries of its biological origins, or music 'more' than a combination of frequencies.

There may indeed be enlightenment to be had from introspective imaginings if we are able to treat them critically—the aesthetic pleasure of doing so, and of understanding ourselves in consequence, is a further pleasure in addition to that of the original artistic experience. But they are also a labyrinth which has swallowed up vast amounts of human energy in the attempt to 'explain' in intuitive terms or treat as revelation the sense of significance which they generate. The result is like the attempt to catch the opaque spots in the optical system of our own eyes—a characteristic activity of the chronically insane—and 'explain' those. Intuitive patterns, unless we are ready to do a great deal of scientific hard work beyond the taste of most artists or most mystics, are better explored for pleasure than for profit. Over this I share Aldous Huxley's anxiety—that someone may succeed in producing the sense of mystical insight artificially as a form of public entertainment. This could bring the rational activities of Man to a standstill, as the search for 'kicks' instead of adult pleasure already threatens to do, while we all sat contemplating the Blakeian landscapes generated by the scanning system in our own heads; unlike the matter of comics, television and films, we should contemplate them with an invincible illusion of enlightenment and merit, while Asia and Africa starved, and the dwarfs who make bombs and conferences played old Harry with our docility unresisted.

Meanwhile we have a fight on our hands. There are, I know, substantial objections to venting our own unconscious aggressions on Authority. But there are also much worse uses to which they could be put. If it is true that in our society only the disturbed produce art, it may also be true that only disturbed rebels will be sufficiently motivated to set effective resistance afoot. It is a poor measure of our sanity if we remain undisturbed by present events. As with artists, and, if they were to be as publicly examined, as with scientists, it is easy enough to trace the reaction-formations which have made social reformers and rebels what they have been. They too are playing, like the rest of us, even when they are willing to die for their game, but like artists and scientists they leave us the concrete products of their play. They, too, are only protagonists. Revolt against the abuse of power is no more pathological in the generality of man than the capacity for art—it is an adaptive character, given the dominance-behaviour which perpetually threatens to disrupt human achievment. Both these capacities are played down by our culture—it would not be surprising if when resistance reasserts itself, so does creativity—and probably in that order.

The Romantic theory of art has always maintained that there is a connection between creation and protest rather of the type implied in Freud's remark about unhappiness and fantasy. Interpreted in this manner, the rubric also includes science. If art is the product of the collision between wish and reality, science is the attempt of wish to control reality—as the price of which it has to accept the discipline of the real—and libertarianism is the rejection of those who will not or cannot accept this discipline, but exercise their uncontrolled wish at our expense. Both art and science have generally been seen by Promethean-Romantic art as a model in which a personified 'Universe', because it does not share our wish, begins as an 'enemy' to be conquered (though it eventually also becomes an environment to be understood). This attitude has often, perhaps always, originated in a reaction-formation similar to Shelley's, but the essential of the model, the identification with humanness against Otherness, has point in itself, as Shelley's own intellectual system had point; it remained intelligible in defining objectives for nineteenth-century science, and still is so, even though the border between self and environment is a fiction which it is now biologically inconvenient to maintain. We need not carry out the final operation in soft-centred ideology and identify the two enemies as biological order on one hand and randomness on the other, though this has real meaning both in Darwinian and in psychological terms, so long as the chief natural 'enemies' of human wish are disease, neurosis, and death.

The demagogic abbreviation of this Romantic or Promethean ideology—the ideology which Shelley extracted with such persistence from his own struggles with wish and reality—is that Man is at odds with Death, inside himself and out, and with those of his own number who support it. This is a soft-centred statement as it stands, and an oversimplification, but it will do, and it is intelligible and capable of hard-centred expansion. That the enactors of fantasy at the expense of others are both theoretically and practically 'allies' of death has never been more alarmingly obvious. We are not obliged to blame them for it—blame, guilt and revenge, as Shelley and Freud both recognise, are ideas characteristic of the public fantasy-enactors' own particular disorder—but we still have to resist them.

On all grounds I think that our best hope of doing so is not so much in stern enthusiasms, which are themselves very often in their 'purposive genuineness' no more than unrecognised play, but in the combativeness of the ordinary man in defence of the things he is always being encouraged to consider unworthy—his food, his skin, his health, his sexual relationships, his rest and his pleasures, which belong to living in earnest: by a sufficiently truculent defence of these he may be able to destroy the public fantasy which now makes inroads on them and prevents the application of science from making them general. There is in this a kind of moral jiu-jitsu which we may have underrated by concentrating on the activist and positive idea of revolution— we now need a revolution which will be activist but negative, to restrain super-individual power, not to expand it—to resist active organisation of one kind in order that we may acquire passive organisation of another. There are no positive issues in contemporary politics—all the live issues are negative issues of resistance: if they can be forced home, if we can stop the nonsense at the top, the positive consequences will arise outside politics, in the sphere of serious activities. We have allowed ourselves to be played with too long.

In the same way we need courage; but only of one kind. If we could exchange the fantasy-courage which talks robustly about the annihilation of Man on principle for a little intelligent and earnest cowardice at the top we might all feel easier in our beds. Even the total lack of principle in party politics and party leaders may prove an exploitable asset—it makes us able to reverse their policies through 180 degrees by threatening their prospects of self-inflation, and we shall run no risk of encountering any block from a sense of duty or a wish for consistency, only from their obsessions, which with skill we can use to control or discredit them.

On Play and Earnest

All over the world there are already signs of public movement which has a common objective, whether it opposes police rule in Hungary, nuclear insanity in Western Europe, or racialism in Africa; the objective in each case is the defeat of the fantasy of power, the replacement of delinquent play by the earnest of mutual aid and unbadgered living; and the method, individual resistance to the requirements of the fantasy-makers. Those movements may, of course, fail, and Mr. Nevil Shute's predictions may be fulfilled in whole or in part—we need no Koestlerian unction in saying that to make us recognise the risk. On the other hand, for reasons I have suggested, the longer the time which passes during which the mental patients can be held in check, the greater the possibility that they will be checked completely, and that science, as the philosophy of earnest as against make-believe, will take a hand compulsorily in attitude-formation. History has a way of disappointing apocalyptic prophecy. I see no less reason—possibly more—to expect this influence to act on the Marxist half of the world, even though its philosophy now debars it, as Christianity once debarred us, from talking sense about the motives of political authority and from recognising the results of the study of the unconscious mind. If the deciding factor turns out to be the direct pressure of practical needs, both cultures may arrive at the same point practically together.

It is interesting to guess what will come next. We might expect, upon form, that the culture of the next 'period' will be chiefly busy with the assimilation into living of what the preceding period, our own, has found out. It may well be relatively quiescent, with little of our impulse to active research. We still do not know for societies, any more than for individual artists or scientists, exactly what effect the withdrawal of compulsive behaviour and of inner anxiety would have on performance, assuming that we could withdraw them. It has been suggested that a culture of Samoans, whose interests are social, sexual, and generally life-centred, must lack the fury of motivation which has operated in Western society since the end of the Middle Ages. Possibly we owe the insatiable curiosity of our explorers and scientists as much to the Victorian ban upon nakedness as to economic or intellectual pressure. We could settle down to be a vast unpuritanical Switzerland. It is in any case difficult to believe that the present exponential growth of knowledge can go on indefinitely without at least a temporary plateau. Interest may indeed shift from research to living, for a while at least, but as a breathing-space rather than a dark age; possibly there will be a simultaneous rejection of the unreal substitutes which take up so much of our culture's technical skills—in favour of real activities, not from puritanism, but from preference.

There are two things which make me doubt that any future post-scientific culture will consist of Samoans—one is the existence of a scientific and intellectual tradition; the other is the impossibility of returning in such a society to any form of intellectual childhood. There is no possibility now of re-creating the state in which there is a hand, other than our own or the next man's, which we can hold—save by an act of renewed self-deception which would offend the new value of hard-centred integrity which we have got from the practice of science. The terms of the attitude-change needed to alter life purposively no longer allow that form of regression—we have undergone a cultural analogue of puberty which is probably irreversible, and that is the one form of play which is no longer permitted to us.

In some ways the traditional Oriental cultures face this problem now. When little or nothing could be done by purposive effort to alter their conditions of life, the individual could be fortified by the rejection of hard-centredness, by the habitual blurring, or by simple non-demarcation, of the line between self and other, between body image and world image, between opposites, between successive cycles of time and successive personal existences; and ideally by the seeking of a complete self-absorption in the not-I which was to be at once solitude and universality, the intrauterine condition. Buddha the Compassionate could send the bereaved mother to find a house in which there had never been a bereavement: if his intention had been to inculcate stoicism, that would have been a profoundly hard-centred counsel. But it was not—his intention was to prove that since involvement causes suffering, absence of suffering can come only from withdrawal. Both in its rejection of a border between self and environment and in its quietism the view of Hindu and of Buddhist cultures is the direct antithesis of the Romantic-Promethean view of human solidarity and struggle *against* absorption in the not-I and in favour of the perpetuation of personal identity; this seems to them hubristic, and, since it cannot ex-hypothesi be won outright, an unrealistic and unearnest wish-fulfilment. This 'despair' is still valid, and the charge of under-lying unrealism is just, but now that betterment is possible by effort, it will no longer do—and once the intellectual standards of activist science are accepted it will never again do, even when no further immediate betterment is possible.

I do not think, in spite of *Brave New World,* that a post-scientific culture, even if it is no longer compulsively activist, will ever be able to return to quietism, either mystical or hedonist, though it may accommodate some of its insights about organic form, non-meddling in observation and the like—Western biology already does so, but with an added dimension of objective intellect which has come to stay. Nor are we likely to be any less aware in the future of the Romantic conviction of struggle, even when it ceases completely to be a mere product of unconscious resentments. We may have learned it originally from the repressed hatreds of the nursery, but it now has more substance than that. Faced with Gautama's choice between suffering with experience and withdrawal without, we have chosen the first. Quietism offends our sense of human solidarity, and I will be surprised if that sense ever becomes less necessary with time. In describing the world after the fall of Zeus, Shelley tried to blend this sense of solidarity with an oceanic pantheism of the Indian type, but the result accords very badly with the logic of Promethean romanticism, and it is to militancy, not quietism, that he returns in his final peroration.

In contrast to Shelley and Huxley alike, I think that a main artistic concern of such a life-centred society set on living in earnest, will be the problem of accommodating in equal earnest the 'insolubles' of experience without being demoralised by them —in the past they have been dealt with by belief, which was in essence play; for thousands of years we have pretended that the dead sleep, that the lost wife or child has only gone on a journey, or, in our time, that if we forget death we will perhaps not die. If art of the kind we know arises by the collision of wish and reality, this is one point where it is always likely to arise with especial intensity. The postponement of death, the removal of illness, the slowing of ageing and the removal of accident will not remove this ultimate collision between the fact of death and the Romantic assertion of personality which is the prerequisite of science, and the source of our control over events and ourselves. The art of a 'Brave New World' which will most closely resemble the art we know is likely for this reason to be concerned with the need to express and discharge grief without intellectual compromise, by providing something our culture is almost wholly without, namely a vehicle for the expression of *mourning*. By comparison with primitive peoples, we have almost forgotten how to mourn—psychiatry has time and again to help grief-weighted individuals to do precisely this by experiencing and giving rein to a biologically essential emotion which they have no idea how to express.

Hemingway, challenged over the gratuitous death of Catherine, replied that there can be no happy end to a marriage between lovers.

A scientific, hard-centred culture with strong erotic interests and a corresponding concentration on personal and family life will require to be able, when necessary, to mourn. It cannot fail to have a strong sense of tragedy, focused on matters which are tragic, not in the Classical, but rather in the colloquial and journalistic sense. In this respect Classical tragedy is already no longer very relevant to modern needs—where there is a tragic ἁμαρτία, the need in the eyes of such a culture is for instruction or for intervention. The fatalist tragedy of the post-Greek tradition is not relevant either. Since we no longer believe in fate, which is the key idea behind the tragic dénouement, we now read *Romeo and Juliet* as a sermon against intolerance, which was not its original intention—intolerance, indeed, did not kill the lovers, only bad luck and self-dramatisation. The prestige sad ending of our own literature is equally false, because it still contains the germ of the idea of payment and of guilt (usually for pleasure) and makes suffering itself the main source of emotional satisfaction—its motives are thus often not very different from the motives behind the clamour for corporal punishment or longer sentences.

The significantly 'tragic' events of our own culture are likely in the future to be more and more those which we do not now write plays about—age, death, sickness, accident, the tragedies of a highly genitalised, hard-centred society which has sharpened their intensity by making them rare, which satisfies all its non-group emotional needs in personal, chiefly erotic, relations—such a society is no country for the old, and its worst evils are bereavement or isolation. It is one thing to lose the morbid fear of death, but quite another to be indifferent to these.

Our society has already a deep need to be able, when necessary, to express unpleasant emotions frankly, but we have no acceptable means of doing so. We have developed the tradition that grief must be passed off (which means, when we no longer believe the passing-off formulae, repressed to our hurt). If we experience it, we have to do so without the support of faith, fate, edification or polyanna—and without Macduff's consolation in having someone to blame. Unless we are able to develop an acceptable artistic or social vehicle for mourning we run the risk of becoming affectless —like the facile people of *Brave New World* or the self-regarding, self-annihilating quietist mystic—both of these being schizoid rather than stoical responses to the danger of having to experience grief; or of avoiding unpleasant emotions at the price of dangerous irrationality. The traditional remedies developed to evade the encounter are too expensive intellectually for adults. If we are to be adult in our personal, sexual and social relations we cannot remain children in our dealings with death and disappointment, which are an equally real part of our biology.

I began this discussion with play, pleasure and pretence, and I am ending it with the ability to accept unpleasant emotion as the final test of earnest. We are, accordingly, back where we started, at the difference between the hard-centred mode, the mode of serious purpose—brought into existence as science by the desire to make ourselves indestructible and the world as we would like it, but obliged in so doing to acquire the self-discipline of reality— and the soft-centred mode of thinking which pretends earnestness but is perpetually and anxiously at play. Unfortunately for man, some of the most important emotional and character-forming responses are acquired at a time in early childhood when the avoidance of unpleasure is automatic; we are apt to spend the rest of our lives in the voluntary pursuit of pain to keep those infant avoidances intact. I have not discussed the Freudian 'death instinct' for a number of reasons—the Darwinian arguments for such an instinct are of a piece with the belief that senescence as a limit to individual life is actively evolved, 'for the benefit of the species', whereas it now appears to be an escape from evolution: Freud in his later years was very pardonably influenced by his own long, painful and exhausting illness, but there is a wide difference between the malignant dynamism of unconscious death-wishes and the willingness of an old man to be done with living: and finally the Thanatos we see expressed in human affairs is not an instinct, in the sense of a complex, function-fulfilling behaviour— it is more often a reaction-formation, expressed in behaviour which simulates earnest in the mind of its proprietor, but is aimless and insightless in fact. In any case, it makes little difference —if there is such an instinct, it requires to be overcome in the pursuit of purposive living; the antithesis between earnest with insight and pretence without it remains the key choice in all forms of human activity. It is now obvious to everyone that if we do not soon prove able to live in earnest, and assert our will to do so against those who have no interest in the real, or in living, we shall die in earnest. The position of science in such a matter should be evident. If art is, as it often asserts, a positive activity deserving our respect and cultivation, it too should be in earnest with insight, even when it is engaged, as its function requires, in valid and satisfying pretence.

Notes

PAGES 1 to 22

[1] Jones, Ernest: *Sigmund Freud—Life and Work*, Vol. III, p. 22 (1957).
[2] Richards, I. A.: *Coleridge on Imagination*. (Routledge, 1934.)
[3] Richards, I. A.: *Science and Poetry*. (Routledge, 1926.)
[4] Richards, I. A.: *Coleridge on Imagination*. (Routledge, 1934.)
[5] Charter Day address, University of Oregon, 1954.
[6] Henn, T. H.: *The Lonely Tower*. (Methuen, 1950.)
[7] Quoted by Michael Tippett, *Moving into Aquarius*. (Routledge, 1959.)

PAGES 23 to 42

[8] Hook, S.: *Psychoanalysis, scientific method and philosophy*. (New York University Press, 1959.)
[9] Kant, Emmanuel: *Dissertation on ethical philosophy*. (1837.)
[10] *Descent of Man*, part I, p. 98.
[11] *Descent of Man*, part I, p. 99, footnote.
[12] *Ibid.*, p. 105.
[13] *Ibid.*, p. 115.
[14] *Ibid.*, III, p. 576.
[15] Tinbergen, N. and Moynihan, N.: *Br. Birds* (1952), 45, 19–22.
[16] Couturier, M.: *L'Ours brun*. (Grenoble, 1954.)
[17] Scheffer, V. B. and Wilke, F. *Growth* (1953), 17, 129.
[18] *Works*, standard edn., Vol. XVII.
[19] Jones, Ernest: *Sigmund Freud—Life and Work*. Vol. II, p. 254 (1955).
[20] Farmer, H. S.: *National Ballad and Song*, III, 62. (1897).
[21] Fenichel, O.: *Coll. Pap.*, series I. (1954.)
[22] Jones, Ernest, *op. cit.*
[23] Jones, Ernest, *op. cit.* II, p. 502.
[24] Hutchinson, G. E.: *Intl. J. Psychoanal.* (1930), 11, 83–86.
[25] Lampl, H. in *Drives, Affects and Behaviours*. (New York University Press 1953.) L. Szekely: *Intl. J. Psychoanal.* (1957), 38, 98.
[26] Donne, John: *Elegies*.
[27] Mitchell, W., Falconer, M. A. and Hill, D.: *Lancet* (1954), ii, 627.
[28] Kallmann, F. J.: *J. new ment. Dis.* (1952), 115, 283; *Am. J. Genet.*, 4, 136.
[29] Hutchinson, G. E.: *Amer. Nat.* (1959), 93, 81.
[30] Comfort, A.: *Amer. Nat.* (1959), 93, 389.

Notes

31 Penrose, L. S.: *Proc. roy. Soc. B.* (1955), **144**, 203.
32 Medawar, P. B.: *The Future of Man.* (1960.)
33 Greenacre, P.: *Psychosomat Child Study* (1953), **8**, 189; *Ibid* (1955), **10**, 184.
34 Clark, Sir Kenneth: *The Nude.* (Murray, 1936.)

PAGES 43 to 73

37 Jung, C. G.: *The archetypes and the collective unconscious.* (1959.)
38 Read, Herbert: *Collected Essays in literary Criticism*, p. 126. (Faber & Faber, 1950.)
39 Read, Herbert: *The True Voice of Feeling.* (Faber & Faber, 1954.)
40 Freud, S.: *Introductory Lectures on psychoanalysis.* (1922.)
41 Jung, C. G.: *The development of personality*, p. 115. (Routledge, 1954.)
42 Read, Herbert: *Collected Essays in literary Criticism*, p. 146. (Faber & Faber, 1950.)
43 Bergler, E.: Psychoanalysis of writers and literary production in Róheim, G.: *Psychoanalysis and the Social Sciences.* (Imago Press, 1947.)
45 Read, Herbert: *Collected Essays in literary Criticism*, p. 140. (Faber & Faber, 1950.)
46 Flaubert, G.: *Lettres*, III, 50. (Paris: Conard, 1926–33.)
47 *La Visite*, in the Urvater Collection.
48 In Claude Mellan's 'Femme à la Souricière' the motif of sexual investigation in these Venus-and-Cupid groups becomes explicit; this piece, which Thuillier calls 'sujet scabreux, mais l'un des plus beaux nus de la peinture française', completes the psychosymbolic circle. The engraving from it is reproduced by Chastel, A.: *Nicolas Poussin.* (C.N.R.S., 1960.)
49 Giedion-Welcker: *Paul Klee*, p. 142. (Faber & Faber, 1952.)
50 Kubie, L. S.: *Neurotic distortion of the creative process.* (Lawrence, Kansas: University of Kansas Press, 1958.)

PAGES 74 to 99

51 Fleming, Ian: *Dr. No.* (London, Cape, 1958.)
52 *New Statesman*, 5 April 1958.
53 *Spectator*, 4 April 1958.
54 Mario Praz: *The Romantic Agony.* (Oxford University Press, 1951.)
55 Eustatius: *Hysminias and Hysmine.*
56 Todd, F. A.: *Some Ancient Novels.* (Oxford University Press, 1940.)
57 Manilius: *Astron.*, **5**, 627 seq.
58 Gorer, Geoffrey: *Bali and Angkor.* (1936.)
59 Quoted by Hoggart, *The Uses of Literacy.*
60 Westermark, E.: *Marriage Ceremonies in Morocco.* (London, Macmillan, 1914.)
61 Fleming, Ian: *Diamonds are Forever.* (Cape, 1956.)
62 G. Legman: *Love and Death.* (1949.)
63 Nordau, M.: *Degeneration*, p. 543. (1895.)
64 Heinlein, R.: *The Puppet-Masters.*

PAGES 100 to 118

65 *Kāma-Kalā—Some notes on the philosophic basis of Hindu erotic sculpture.* Mulk-Raj Anand. (Geneva: Nagel, 1958.)
66 Reeves, James: *The Idiom of the People.* (Heinemann, 1958.)
67 Williams, Sir Monier: *Brahmanism and Hinduism.* (Murray, 1891.)

Notes

[68] Vallée Poussin, L. de la: art. 'Tantrism' in *Ency. Religion and Ethics* (1921.) For other accounts of these sects see also Needham, J.: *Science and Civilisation in China*, Vol. II. (Oxford University Press, 1956.) Eliade, M.: *Yoga: immortality and freedom*. (Routledge, 1958.) Snellgrove, D. L.: *The Hevajra-Tantra: a critical study*. (Oxford University Press, 1959.) Anon (Kassandas Mulji): *The sect of Maharajas or Vallabhacharyas in Western India* (a very hostile account, by a Hindu of another sect). (London: Trübner, 1865.) Bhandakar, Sir R. G.: *Vaisnavism, Saivism and minor religious systems. Grundr. Indoarischen Phil. u. Altertumskunde* b. 3. heft 6 (Strassburg: Trübner, 1913.) Krishna Deva: The Temples of Khajuraho in Central India. *Ancient India*, 1959, 15, 43–65 (architecture, iconography and history). Franger, W.: *The Millenium of Hieronymus Bosch* (European sects of the same kind). (Faber & Faber, 1952.)

[69] Schmidt, R.: *Beiträge zur indischen Erotik*. (Berlin: 1911.)
[70] Wertham, F.: *Seduction of the innocent*. (Jarrolds, 1955.)

PAGES 119 to 135

[71] Hall, R. A.: Pidgin Languages. *Scientific American* (1959), 200, 124–34.

PAGES 136 to 165

[72] It has—in Jean Genêt's *"Le Balcon."*
[73] Reiwald, P.: *Society and its Criminals*. (Heinemann, 1949.)

Index of Names

Index of Names